NATURAL HISTORY MUSEUM

Diamonds

The world's most dazzling exhibition

Natural History Museum, London

8 July 2005 – 26 February 2006

Acknowledgements

This publication is the catalogue of the *Diamonds* exhibition, 8 July 2005–26 February 2006, originally created by the Natural History Museum, London, under the administration of Dr Michael Dixon.

The exhibition would not have been possible without the generous support of principal sponsor, the Steinmetz Diamond Group, and additional support from the Diamond Trading Company Limited.

The organisers would like to extend their grateful thanks to the lenders of the exhibition:

Aber Diamond Corp.; Rijksmuseum, Amsterdam; Diamond Museum, Province of Antwerp; Aurora Gems Inc.; B & W Group; British Museum; Brinkhaus Jewelers; Daniel Brush; Carnet; Cartier; Cool Diamonds; Cora Diamond Corp.; Dali Diamonds; De Beers LV; the Diamond Trading Company Limited.; Staatliche Kunstsammlungen Grünes Gewölbe, Dresden; Element Six Ltd; the government of the Republic of South Africa; Her Majesty The Queen; Scott Henshall; Valeri Jerlitsyn; The al-Sabah Collection, Dar al-Athar al-Islamiyyah, Kuwait; Shaun Leane; Fred Leighton Rare Collectible Jewels; Diamonds Electronics Group, University College London; Marjan Diamonds; Mouawad (Geneva); Moussaieff Jewellers; Premier Gem Corp.; JAR, Paris; J. Dennis Petimezas; Cornelia Rating; SIBA Corp.; Smithsonian Institution; The Steinmetz Diamond Group; Tiret; Victoria and Albert Museum; Harry Winston; Janet Zapata; J. Zeberg Antiques nv; Benjamin Zucker; and the many private collectors.

The Natural History Museum is grateful to Her Majesty's government for its help in agreeing to indemnify this exhibition under the National Heritage Act 1980, and to MLA for its help in arranging this indemnity.

Many individuals and institutions have given generously of their time and we would like to extend our warmest thanks to all of them, in particular:

Wim Luyckx of the Diamond Museum, Province of Antwerp; René Brus; Renée Frank and Pascal Milhaud of Cartier; Lesley Coldham, David Johnson, Duncan Cooper, Celina Bublik, Tiffany Carlsen and Chris Alderman of the Diamond Trading Company; Christopher Ogilvie-Thompson, Andreas Anker and Chris Wort at Element Six Ltd.; Tom Moses, Elise B. Misiorowski and their colleagues at the Gemological Institute of America; John Nels Hatleberg; Nigel Israel; Richard Jackman of the London Centre for Nanotechnology, University College London; George Harlow of the American Museum of Natural History, New York; Geoffrey Munn and Katherine Purcell at Wartski's; Jeffrey E. Post at the Smithsonian Institution, Washington DC and Janet Zapata.

Natural History Museum staff and consultants involved in the exhibition:

Rachael Casstles; Andrew Fleet, Keeper of Mineralogy; Alan Hart, Head of Collections, Mineralogy; their colleagues, Mahesh Anand, Sara Russell and Frances Wall; Martyn Surridge; Colin Bowles Ltd. (mount-making); Sam Clark (DBA Ltd.); Mike Cook (DBA Ltd.); Halahan Associates (conservators); Deirdre Janson-Smith; Real Studios (exhibition design) and Jan Walgrave, Honorary Director of the Antwerp Province Museums.

Contents

Director's foreword

Diamonds at the Natural History Museum is a landmark on the UK's cultural landscape, bringing a once-in-a-lifetime opportunity to view a quite extraordinary range of the world's most rare and precious stones. For the Museum, *Diamonds* is also the first blockbuster exhibition to open in our newly enlarged temporary exhibitions gallery. The size and diversity of the diamonds we have assembled promise an awe-inspiring experience. But why is the Museum the right venue for this spectacle and why is now the right time for us to undertake this project?

Firstly, the Museum's scientific and cultural mission is founded on our collections. We are one of the world's leading treasurehouses and, in the context of *Diamonds*, the UK's principal repository of mineralogical specimens. But the collection exists for far more than posterity. It is an active research infrastructure, used constantly in the cause of groundbreaking scientific enquiry. It is this that places us uniquely to host such a major event.

Secondly, the Natural History Museum exists to tell the story of the power of nature – a power more clearly encapsulated by diamonds than by any other natural creation. The exhibition conveys the remarkable and thought-provoking qualities of diamonds, from their status as nature's hardest substance to the rarity of coloured stones, one for every 10,000 'white' ones.

Finally, at a time when public interest in celebrity and fashion is at its highest, we at the Museum are best placed to go one step further – to portray the full range of fascinating stories and challenging issues that lie behind this stone that has a unique hold on the popular imagination.

That is precisely what we have set out to do, to tell the complex story of diamonds: from catwalk fashion and dazzling jewellery to futuristic technologies; from tales of historical intrigue to the pain of contemporary conflict. We have searched the globe to bring together this spectacular event. As we have done so, we have been increasingly amazed by one simple fact: the fascination with diamond's power and romance binds us all across time and distance.

While we believe the Museum is singularly equipped to stage *Diamonds*, we could not have contemplated such an undertaking without the generous support of our principal sponsor, the Steinmetz Diamond Group, and additional support from the Diamond Trading Company. Their active and enthusiastic backing has been invaluable and I am deeply grateful to them for helping make the exhibition possible.

As with all major international exhibitions, securing the loan of specimens has been at the heart of our curatorial challenge. The generosity of those lenders who have shared our vision of a truly great exhibition has been fantastic and our thanks are extended to every one of them.

Finally, my personal thanks to the many individuals who have brought this wonderful show to the Museum. They are too numerous to mention, but the result of their effort and creativity is now there for all to see. We hope all our visitors enjoy *Diamonds* as much as we have enjoyed bringing it about.

Michael Dixon
Director, Natural History Museum

Selection of diamond crystals from the Natural History Museum collections.

Sponsors' forewords

With more than seven decades of experience in creating and marketing some of the world's finest diamonds, Steinmetz has strived to make these gems both meaningful and relevant to people around the world. The vision of the Group has always been 'to fuel consumer passion for diamonds through innovative and fresh ideas'. This is why our diamonds make their presence known at the most unique places – be it amidst the roar of Formula One cars at Monaco or at the awe-inspiring Temple of Dawn in Bangkok.

It is with this aim in mind that Steinmetz recognised museums as a source of expertise to disseminate insights and knowledge about this great gem. While diamonds are visible in every shop and corner of the world, it is only within the context of a museum that consumers can comprehend the true value of diamonds – in history and in all walks of life. Our first attempt in this direction was in 2003 with the *Splendor of Diamonds* exhibition at the Smithsonian's National Museum of Natural History, Washington DC. The exhibition succeeded in creating widespread awareness of coloured diamonds, in the United States and around the world.

But the story of a diamond is much bigger, and Steinmetz felt a larger canvas was required to capture its fascinating journey from mine to finger. It is an honour, therefore, to help make this vision come true at the *Diamonds* exhibition along with our partners, the Natural History Museum and the Diamond Trading Company Limited. Only the combined expertise of our partners in their specific fields has helped create this first-of-its-kind exhibition. We hope that through our joint efforts, *Diamonds* will delight, amaze and most importantly bring to life the magic of diamonds for all its visitors.

The Steinmetz Diamond Group

The Diamond Trading Company (DTC) is the sales and marketing arm of the De Beers Group. We are the world's largest source of rough diamonds, handling approximately half the global supply. Recognised internationally by our advertising promise 'A Diamond is Forever', the DTC has a passion and commitment to diamonds and to consumers. As part of the De Beers Group, we are involved in the life of a diamond from the moment it is discovered in the earth, using our 115 years of diamond expertise and marketing knowledge to help consumers feel more confident when making their diamond purchase.

In addition, we have developed significant initiatives to improve the diamond industry's standards of operation, ensuring ethical and professional practices are upheld at all times. We also believe the diamond industry should benefit all those involved and provide a lasting contribution to the communities in which they operate.

It is because of our passion for diamonds and our commitment to the industry, that the DTC is supporting *Diamonds* at the Natural History Museum. We are delighted to be a part of this unique exhibition, along with the Steinmetz Diamond Group, as it celebrates the wonder, magic and allure of diamonds. And, we hope all those who experience it will leave with the same passion and commitment that we have for these remarkable gemstones.

The Diamond Trading Company

The 14-carat fancy vivid blue pear-shaped Blue Empress is an exceptionally rare naturally coloured diamond.

The science of diamonds

Diamonds are pure, or nearly pure, carbon. Carbon is the stuff of life and the fourth most abundant element in the solar system. All living organisms we know are made up of carbon compounds. It is in the air we breathe, mainly as carbon dioxide, and is dissolved in seas, rivers and lakes. Carbon compounds help give soils their fertility, carbon-containing minerals provide the frameworks of coral reefs and make up the limestones of cliffs and mountains, and carbon combined with hydrogen supplies us with oil and gas. So, if carbon is us, and all around us, why are diamonds so rare and thus so highly prized?

Diamonds are rare for three reasons: they form deep within the Earth, they only form in very localised areas beneath the continents, and it takes an extremely rare kind of volcanic activity to bring them to the surface. Although their rarity means all diamonds are valuable, only about 20% of those mined are of gem quality. The remainder are used for a variety of industrial purposes (see *The technology of diamonds*).

Most diamonds that are mined formed at depths of 140–200 kilometres near the base of the tectonic plates that make up the outermost skin of the Earth. The plates only reach such thicknesses below cratons, the oldest parts of the continents; generally plates are 30 kilometres thick or less below the oceans and about 70 kilometres thick under the continents. Cratons have undergone little geological change for at least the past two and a half billion years. The processes that caused the thickening of these old, geologically stable areas ensured that some of the carbon in the plates was carried to great depths. There, diamonds could form at

unimaginable pressures of more than 45,000 times that of the Earth's atmosphere and furnace-like temperatures above 950°C. At shallower depths, under lower pressures and temperatures, pure carbon remains in the form of soft graphite, the material of pencil lead. Diamond formation may have been favoured by conditions that occurred in the relatively young Earth because many, though not all, diamonds which are mined formed around three billion years ago when the Earth was just one third its present age.

Diamonds are brought to the surface from the deep roots of cratons by rare types of volcanic eruptions of magmas (molten rock) rich in dissolved carbon dioxide. These magmas originate in the Earth at depths of more than 150 kilometres, probably at the base of, or just below, the thickened plates of the cratons, far deeper than where other volcanic magmas originate at depths of 60 kilometres or less. The magmas find their way through fractures in the overlying rock and pick up pieces of these rocks as they ascend. Some, but only a few, pick up diamonds.

The magmas begin rising at the speed of a slow-moving car (10–30 km/hour) and end it travelling up to 100 times faster. This acceleration is essential in ensuring the diamonds neither change into graphite as the pressure and temperature decrease nor are oxidised to carbon dioxide. Initially, the magma is about as viscous as toothpaste. As it nears the surface, the pressure lessens and as a result carbon dioxide dissolved in the magma rapidly comes out of solution like that of a freshly opened bottle of champagne. This speeds up the ascent and forms an explosive mix that punches its way to the surface. From following planar fractures at several

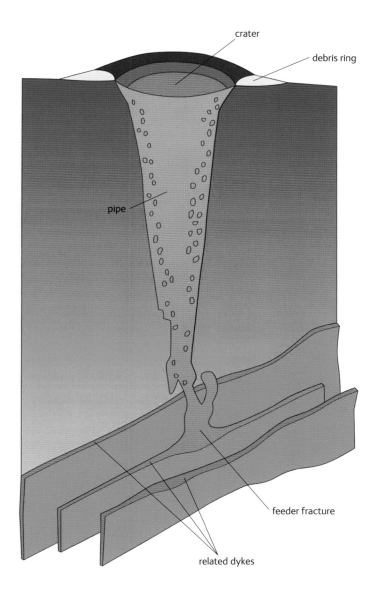

crater

debris ring

pipe

feeder fracture

related dykes

Diagram of a kimberlite pipe showing its root at a depth of about 2.5 km above the planar fractures through which the magma travelled from depth.

kilometres depth, the magma finally blasts its way to the surface forming a carrot-shaped 'pipe'. Different eruptions may follow one another through the same pipe at intervals from days to millions of years apart. Such eruptions have occurred throughout the Earth's history and are not linked to the process of diamond formation. For example, those that brought the diamonds of South Africa to the surface erupted during the past 100 million years, long after the formation of the diamonds which they contain. Only about 6000 pipes formed by such eruptions are known and only about one in 200 pipes contains diamonds in economic quantities. No one has ever seen this type of eruption, and the last occurred about 47 million years ago.

The volcanic rocks that result from these deep-sourced eruptions are called kimberlites and lamproites (kimberlite after Kimberley the birthplace of the South African diamond industry). They form only small volcanoes. The largest kimberlite volcano, Mwadui in Tanzania, is only 146 hectares in area, just 2% the size of Mount St Helens. The volcanoes have shallow craters surrounded by low rings of debris thrown out by the volcano. This debris is relatively easily eroded by running water and material from the rings is washed back to fill in the crater and is also carried away by streams and rivers. With time, the pipes themselves are eroded or covered by sediments such as desert sands or debris from ice sheets, as is the case with the rich diamond-bearing pipes discovered in Canada in the 1990s.

The sediments carried away from pipes may contain diamonds and these are either incorporated into the sands and gravels of rivers, known as alluvial deposits, or transported to the sea where they may be carried along the coast or across the seafloor by prevailing currents. For many centuries the only major source of diamonds were river sediments of southern India particularly those from around the town of Golconda, which gives its name to, and is famous for, the highly transparent type of diamond found there. Just as this Indian source was exhausted, diamonds were discovered in Brazil in the early seventeenth century and these also came from alluvial deposits. Similarly when the diamond 'rush' began in South Africa in the 1860s, it was triggered by alluvial diamonds. It was only in 1871 that diamonds began being mined from 'dry land' when the kimberlite pipes of South Africa were found.

Everything about the formation of diamonds and kimberlite pipes makes diamonds difficult to find. The formation of diamonds below cratons means they are restricted to limited areas of the continents, notably parts of southern Africa, Russia, Australia, eastern South America, Canada and southern India. Even within these areas the targets for exploration companies are the rare pipes of kimberlite or lamproite and these themselves are often buried by younger sediments. The first diamond-bearing pipes were found in South Africa by prospectors widening their search for diamonds away from river deposits and following up chance finds made by local people. Today scientific methods of chemical analysis and geophysics are used to locate the pipes.

Chemical analysis is used to identify 'indicator' minerals in sediments and soils above and downstream from where pipes may occur. Indicator minerals are ones that formed deep in the Earth

Octahedron of 'rough' diamond, about 1 cm across, in kimberlite from Kimberley, South Africa.

together with diamonds and were brought to the surface along with the diamonds. Some garnets are an important indicator mineral for diamonds, but only those garnets with a particular composition that research has shown form with diamonds. Other minerals that form under the high-pressure and high-temperature conditions of the deep Earth, like certain chromites and pyroxenes, indicate the likely presence of a pipe rather than diamonds themselves. Another mineral, ilmenite, differs in composition from pipe to pipe so finding ilmenites of, say, three distinct compositions indicates the presence of three pipes. No one indicator mineral gives all the answers, but a suite of them found together suggests the presence of a pipe somewhere upstream and points explorers in the right direction.

Geophysical tools can be used to identify where pipes are located. These instruments may be probes in the ground that measure the Earth's electrical resistivity or devices carried by planes that measure the strength of the magnetic field. Whatever the tool, the objective is to look for mappable anomalous results caused by the presence of a pipe, that has contrasting properties to those of the surrounding rock. With careful processing of the data gathered, the presence of a pipe is indicated on a data map by a strongly coloured circle in a sea of other coloured contours.

Even when located, very few pipes contain diamonds in economic quantities for mining. Samples from across a pipe have to be retrieved by drilling to prove the presence of diamonds in sufficient quantities to justify investing in a mine. Even then there will be an element of uncertainty, and hence of risk, in any mining operation. Something like 0.8 grammes (four carats) of diamonds in every tonne of rock is a high grade of discovery (a carat is the standard unit of weight used for gemstones: 1 carat = 0.2 grammes). Finding river or marine sands and gravels with sufficient diamonds to justify an extraction operation involves similar careful exploration, sampling, evaluation and risk.

The carbon from which most diamonds formed was incorporated, at the time of the Earth's formation, into the thick layer called the mantle, which developed between the Earth's thin outer crust and core. The lowermost part of the tectonic plates is made up of mantle and, in the roots of cratons, it is within this mantle material made up predominantly of the minerals olivine and pyroxene that most mined diamonds formed at 140–200 kilometres. However, not all diamonds from the Earth's interior have formed from primordial mantle carbon. A minority are derived from the carbon of organisms and carbonate minerals formed at the Earth's surface, which has been carried into the mantle by descending tectonic plates and brought back again by kimberlite and lamproite volcanoes. These diamonds are associated with eclogite, a rock consisting of the minerals garnet and pyroxene, which formed from ocean-floor lavas carried in the descending plates. Eclogite boulders in kimberlite pipes may be very rich in diamonds with as much as 10% of their weight being made up of diamond.

Even rarer than the diamonds formed in plates which have been subducted (i.e. descended) into the mantle are diamonds formed where continents have collided because of plate tectonic processes. Occasionally, these collisions have carried carbon-containing surface rocks to great depths. There they have experienced the ultra-high pressures necessary to form diamonds before being brought rapidly to the surface by the plate tectonic forces with their diamonds still intact. Such diamonds, though, are very small measuring only a few tens of microns in size (a human hair is about 100 microns across).

Over the past 20 years or so scientists studying diamonds have discovered that not all formed near the base of the tectonic plates. A few formed at even greater depths, some at least as deep as 700 kilometres. These are invaluable as they provide the only samples from deep within the mantle. They often contain tiny pieces of minerals, known as inclusions, which have been incorporated in the

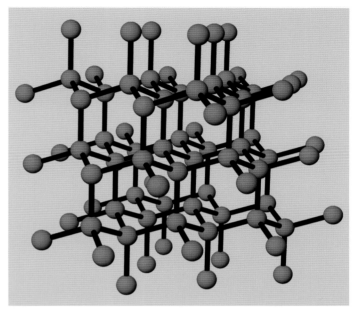

Diamond structure. Each sphere represents a carbon atom and the connecting rods represent the bonds between them. In reality the atoms are densely packed together, not apart as in this 'exploded' view.

diamond as it has crystallized from the surrounding mantle. Although the inclusions generally measure only a few tenths of a millimetre in size they can be studied to give us clues as to what the Earth is like at depths of hundreds of kilometres. They tell us that the mantle down to about 650 kilometres has old ocean floor, carried there by descending plates, mixed in with its constituent peridotite which formed as the Earth grew. They also suggest the lower mantle beneath is largely peridotite although some slabs of ocean floor may have penetrated into it to depths of 700 kilometres or more.

The ultimate sources of all the carbon incorporated into the growing Earth were stars, which grew and disintegrated before the solar system came into being 4.56 billion years ago. The carbon was formed within the stars from hydrogen and helium, by a process known as nucleosynthesis, at temperatures and pressures far in excess of those in planets such as Earth. Over the history of the solar system, most of its carbon has taken part in innumerable reactions and processes. Some, though, is found in the same form as it was when it was incorporated into the solar system. This includes carbon in nanometre-sized diamonds found in 'primitive' meteorites consisting of the virtually unaltered material from which the solar system formed. These diamonds are rarest of all those we know. They are samples of the universe from before the solar system. Beyond the solar system, astrophysicists find other evidence of diamonds in stars. One recent discovery suggests a 4000-kilometre-wide 'white dwarf' (a collapsed star) in the Centaurus galaxy consists of diamond.

While some meteorites contain very small diamonds dating from before the solar system, others have created diamonds on impact with the Earth by generating high pressures, shock waves and vaporisation. For example, the quarried rock that makes up the town walls of Ries in Germany contains tiny diamonds generated when the area was hit by a meteorite 15 million years ago.

Whether formed beneath a craton, deeper in the mantle, in a star or by meteorite impact, diamonds are set apart from other minerals because they may be worked to reveal great beauty and possess a unique combination of properties. Both attributes stem from their structure. The carbon atoms that make up diamond are densely packed in a regular array held together by strong bonds. This is reflected in the relatively high density and extreme hardness of diamond.

Although diamond is the hardest natural material known, its structure allows it to be perfectly cleaved in four directions. This property is exploited by cutters who, in producing gemstones from mined 'rough' diamonds, unlock the visual properties of the stone which themselves result from the dense structure of diamond. The cutter uses the intense optical properties of diamond in the way it reflects, bends and disperses light to achieve the maximum brilliance and 'fire' of the final cut gem.

Conventionally diamonds have been valued for being colourless and clear. At times, though, coloured stones have been fashionable. So-called 'fancy coloured' diamonds are rare: estimates suggest that, depending on the source, between about one in every 500 to one in every 10,000 gem-quality diamonds is coloured. The colour in diamonds results from the presence of tiny amounts of elements other than carbon or from atomic-scale defects in the diamond structure. The presence of nitrogen, for instance, gives yellow hues and of boron, blue hues. Pinks and reds result from defects in the atomic structure. Green diamonds are produced by radiation damage of the structure, a rare natural phenomenon that can be imitated in the laboratory. Black diamonds are 'coloured' by the presence of mineral inclusions or can be produced by irradiation.

As well as those properties that make diamonds the first among gemstones, there are others which in combination set diamond out as an important material for modern technology. Its high thermal conductivity is one such property. It is this that makes a diamond 'icy' to the lips and adds to the mystique of the stone (see *The technology of diamonds*).

Diamond's rarity, beauty and utility, then, are dictated by the conditions of its formation and the atomic structure which results from these conditions. Diamonds may be just carbon, but carbon forged in a wondrous fashion.

Andrew Fleet and Alan Hart
Mineralogy Department, Natural History Museum

Diamond jewellery in Europe

The beginning

Diamond is the rarest, most durable and prestigious gemstone ever to be used in jewellery. Charged with symbolic meaning, it has a particularly distinctive power, one that speaks to our imaginations. Diamond used in jewellery depicting a rose, a branch of ivy leaves or two doves, symbolises affection. This symbolism has a heightened intensity because diamond also signifies durability. The generous giver doesn't only love his beloved at the moment of giving the gift, he vows to love her forever.

Diamond was not always appreciated for its brilliance, since this quality only became apparent through expert polishing, and it wasn't until the end of the sixteenth century that the techniques were mastered fully in Europe.

Diamonds have been known in Europe since Classical times. This we learn from the writings of Gaius Plinius Secundus (died AD 79), better known as Pliny the Elder: 'a diamond – of the greatest rarity and desirability – would protect the wearer from poison and sickness, as well as from madness and mortal fear'. (See Roman ring, *Cat. 68*). Like so many other cultural and technical achievements, after the fall of the Roman Empire in the West, diamond was largely forgotten about. After the Crusades, trade relations were established with the Orient, allowing caravans to travel to India. Together with a general return of interest in gemstones, the diamond made a comeback, with people believing again in its extraordinary strength and amulet qualities.

In the fifteenth century, some progress in processing diamond was made, and diamonds began to symbolise the unbreakable bond of a relationship, playing an important role in pendants, brooches, rings, often placed alongside rubies and pearls, which stand for passion and purity. The interest in diamonds spread, due to the greater desire for luxury within the royal courts. The qualities that were attributed to gems were assumed by kings and queens and, of course, also adapted to their needs. If diamond kept sickness away, as Pliny alleged, then the diamond wearer would be invincible. Therefore, diamond is still the stone of choice for royalty. Powerful families such as the Medicis of Florence placed pointed diamonds in their emblem. Indeed, many early jewels included diamonds in their raw form, barely cut and in the natural octahedron shape (see natural crystal ring, *Cat. 69*). They were rather cumbersome stones at that time, with sharp edges that could scratch, tear and damage. An increasing number of table-cut diamonds then also began to appear: the top of the diamond would be cleaved off, a technique that presumably came from India. Gold was the only setting used for diamonds; silver would come later at the end of the seventeenth century, when people judged its white shine more convenient for the facetted rose-cut stones.

During the sixteenth century, the wealth of the ruling classes grew exponentially, thanks to the treasures that flowed into State coffers, following the discoveries in Africa, America and the Orient. Jewellery enjoyed great refinement in the Mannerism period, a style of sixteenth-century art characterised by unusual effects of scale, lighting and perspective. Spain dominated European politics at the time, and its influence spread to jewellery, strict and rigid designs but extremely rich, with an abundance of necklaces, pendants, waist-chains, bracelets, brooches, rings, earrings, aigrettes on the hat or the hair. Like many other forms of art, the religious inspiration was abundant, giving birth to typical jewels such as cross pendants (*Cat. 25, 26*). The virtuoso masters combined gold with enamelling, precious stones and pearls (*Cat. 25*). In that period Antwerp, Paris and some north Italian cities were the main market and processing centres for diamonds.

New fashions

In the seventeenth century, the demand for diamond jewellery grew again, sparkling with the newly introduced rose cut. Its production became an international affair, thanks to book printing, with drawings from gifted designers such as Virgil Solis and Erasmus Hornick, both from Nurenberg, Hans Collaert from Antwerp, and later the Frenchmen Daniel Mignot and Balthasar Lemercier.

Again the evolution of fashion played an important role in sculpting the designs of diamond. The Spanish supremacy in politics came to an end and France took the leading role. Fashion liberated itself from the restrictions of Spain's influence. Although diamond jewellery became less colourful with the decreased use of enamel and other gems, it sparkled all the more and the diamond as we know it today was born (see *Cat. 28, 29*).

Under French influence, the candlelit parties of the rich dazzled with diamonds (see *Cat. 30*). The rose cut shone the most, encouraging wearers of the older table cuts to have them recut to add more facets and so shine even more. Parisian chroniclers in the 1660s complained that the eagerness of ladies to recut their diamonds had ruined them, and predicted the trend would be

Jean-Baptiste Tavernier by Nicolas de Largillière, *c.* 1670. A French traveller and diamond merchant, Tavernier sold many important stones to the French court. His account of his travels in India includes drawings of some of the most famous diamonds ever found.

short-lived. They were seriously mistaken, because from the trend to add facets to table-cut stones came the most popular cut of all – the brilliant.

France was the place to be for diamonds. The inventory of 1610 of the valuables of Queen Marie de Medici recorded some 11,500 diamonds, plus another 4000 'negligible' little ones. King Louis XIII was mad about diamond clothing accessories and possessed a few hundred diamond buttons. Cardinal Mazarin (1602–1661), first minister to Louis XIV, was a great diamond fancier. Altogether he purchased 18 extraordinary stones that were among the best money could buy. He bought most of them from Jean-Baptiste Tavernier, a French traveller and diamond merchant who visited India several times and published a book about it (see *Cat. 14*). Mazarin bequeathed them to the French crown, and several were used in the jewels of Empress Eugenie, 200 years later. A few can still be seen in the Louvre, Paris. Indeed, from the seventeenth century on, rulers understanding that wealth meant power wanted to display theirs, to demonstrate their authority, and diamonds became more established as a must for crown jewels. No sovereign crown escaped the necessity to hold diamonds. The largest and most valuable stones were at home in regalia – the crown, sceptre and globe with a cross – and were increased in number by the sovereign as a symbol of their might. No wonder almost all great diamond jewellery collections were originally in royal or imperial possession: the Dresden 'Green Vault' Museum, the Stately Hermitage Museum in Saint-Petersburg, the Moscow Kremlin, the Lisbon Palacia da Ajuda Museum and the Munich Residenz Museum. The British Royal family is famous for its phenomenal jewellery collection.

From its origins as an amulet protecting against sickness and poisoning – scarcely crafted but still sought after, intriguing and costly – diamond evolved to become a glittering, facetted symbol of sovereign power for the head of State, for well-off nobility and patricians. Even though it was now utterly lacking in superstitious connotations, diamond was a means to disseminate their high status.

A king's best friend

Around 1700 a shortage of diamonds began to weigh on the production of new jewels. The mines in India became slowly exhausted. New stones were provided by the re-cutting of old table-cut gems into brilliants, whereby they naturally ended up in new jewels. It was a great relief when, after the middle of the 1720s – one is not sure exactly when – news reached Europe that diamonds had been found in Brazil in the region of Minas Geraes. Brazil at that time was a Portuguese colony so the king of Portugal immediately seized on the discovery and organised the distribution and sale of the diamonds. It was mainly the Dutch merchants who obtained a concession, as the hub of the diamond industry was then Amsterdam.

The supply of new diamonds provoked a race throughout the eighteenth century between various dynasties to obtain the best diamonds with the greatest sparkle. At the court of the King of Lisbon, of the Saxes and the Poles, that of the Russians and in France, the most beautiful diamonds were used by the best jewellers in the most lavish settings. Men wore diamonds certainly as much as women. Apart from buttons, epaulettes, shoe buckles and hat aigrettes, noblemen also had their order insignia lavishly decorated with diamonds (see *Cat. 31–39*).

The style of the jewels worn by women in particular changed radically in the course of the eighteenth century. Little remained of the stylised and symmetrical designs from the century before. The preference now was for very naturalistic jewellery, influenced by the widespread ideas of the philosopher Jean-Jacques Rousseau (1712–1778). The wonderful hand-coloured etchings of natural scientists such as Georges-Louis, Count of Buffon (1707–1788) and the Swede Carl Linnaeus (1707–1778) also prompted the return to nature (see *Cat. 41*). Fabulous corsage jewels were made, most suggesting flowers and sprays, or large bows (see *Cat. 31*). They are visible on many portraits, but unfortunately few or none of those jewels have survived to this time. Once the fashion changed, the large jewel was taken apart and the stones re-used.

Napoleon's diamonds

On 14 July 1789, the Parisian resurgents stormed the Bastille. In a short period of time the ancient feudal rights were abolished, and the king and queen were executed. The tribunal of the revolution pursued the noblefolk without exception. It was a dark time for artists, dependent on commissions from the church and the nobility. However, Napoleon would soon seize power, end the pursuit of the nobility and the clergy and, once crowned as Emperor on 2 December 1804, would reverse the revolution significantly through his absolute power and his love of ostentation.

In 1808, he founded a new nobility class, the Noblesse Impériale, and rewarded his generals and other devoted allies with newly created titles such as 'duke', and 'count', and sought reconciliation with the old nobility. He showered both his empresses and the women in his entourage with opulent jewels, for which he used some fabulous gemstones, especially diamonds, from the previous royal possessions. In the meantime the Empire style had made its entrance, under the influence of Classicism. The Empire introduced a specific piece of jewellery of antique origin: the diadem or tiara (see later diadems *Cat. 52, 61*). The diadems were always made with diamonds and other precious stones that in a stylised floral motif created a relief at the top. But there were also tiaras of a stricter design, with cameos – another influence from the past – instead of gemstones.

Queens and princesses wore little crowns around a twist of hair behind their tiara, and sometimes a decorative comb as well. But one must not forget the other pieces from this time: the rivière, a necklace with just a series of diamonds strung together, *en chute*, from the neck at both sides becoming larger towards the front (*Cat. 51*), or a necklace with spread out pendeloques, and finally bracelets and earrings.

The empire of Napoleon I did not last long. After the battle of Waterloo, 18 June 1815, the victors installed the Restoration, whereby the Bourbons, who had ruled before the French Revolution, again took a place on the throne of France first headed by Louis XVIII, then Charles X. The nobility was revived, and its members picked up the customs and tastes of the previous generation. And so many jewels, inspired by flowers, were again created as they had been in the eighteenth century. The major difference was that what was gained in the Empire was not relinquished: the diadem had gained a permanent and important place.

Romanticism

Classicism was followed by Romanticism, with a broad interest in the past and everything that had to do with the expression of sentiment. Some exaggeration did occur, which in turn lead to sentimentalism. The symbolism of flowers was then a hobby for many English that spread over to the continent. Queen Victoria (1819–1837–1901) also had a penchant for flowers and garden culture. Lists of flowers and plants were published, sometimes with more than 600 varieties, in which their significance was described. This significance was applied to the jewellery. In this way a girl from a good family would be given a *corbeille de noces* by her suitor's family: a basket with beautiful presents, always with jewels, that emphasised the connection between the two youngsters, but also between the families. The diamond diadem was made very naturalistic with strong flower motifs: oak leaves for fertility and strength, forget-me-nots hoping for permanent attention, eglantine or wild roses for spontaneous love.

The diamond jewels from around the middle of the nineteenth century are consistently florally stylised. Some heavy brooches carry 'pampilles', strings of diamonds hanging beneath each other, for which the inspiration is again floral. They represent bushes and trees that produce a sort of stringy blossom or catkin, a sign of energy and fertility (Cat. 52–56). The jewellers become increasingly inventive and dreamt up jewels for various uses. As a result, many tiaras could also be used as a necklace, when dismounted from the frame. Others could be subdivided into various brooches. Large brooches could be split in three, so ladies could go to tea with a small one, and in the evening appear at a party with a large floral spray. The disadvantage for the continued existence of these jewels is as with the parures, sets of jewels intended to be worn together: the children divide the jewels between them on inheritance.

Floral jewels 'blossomed' as never before. Empress Eugénie of France (1826–1853–1920), who owned an enormous amount of jewellery, nurtured a great appreciation for the unfortunate Queen Marie-Antoinette, who was beheaded by the French revolutionaries in 1793. Her preference for large, natural brooches was taken up and propagated by the Empress as the 'Marie-Antoinette' style (see her veneration for Queen Marie-Antoinette Cat. 62).

But jewellery art began to be hampered once more by a shortage of diamonds. The Brazilian mines were producing less, and in Europe a new clientele had evolved because of the industrial revolution: in mining, the shipping industry, the railways and the factories. The poverty in the cities was merely a backdrop to the immeasurable fortunes of the grand industrials. They mirrored themselves in the aristocracy, built castles and offered their wives, daughters and mistresses costly jewels.

South Africa at last

So again there was a sigh of relief when, in 1867, at the world exhibition of Paris the first diamond from South Africa was presented, the Eureka (Cat. 58). After the French-Prussian war of 1870–71, African diamonds flooded the market, to the great satisfaction of the notorious jewellery houses. The rise of the large jewellery houses thus began, almost all these firms lasting until after the Belle Epoque, the hey-day of Parisian indulgence, towards the end of the nineteenth century. Some of them continue to this day, providing jewellery for the very rich, most having their headquarters in Paris. The house Mellerio dits Meller has its origins in seventeenth-century Lombardy. The Bapst dynasty worked for the last kings of France, as well as for its last emperor. Chaumet was in 1889 the follower of Nitot, who already made jewels for Napoleon I and his court. Cartier was already established in 1847, Boucheron in 1858. The founders of Van Cleef & Arpels, from Amsterdam, enjoyed its ascendancy to the top after the First World War. The house Bulgari, from Greek origin, has been in Rome since 1881. From the mid nineteenth century, Tiffany and Co. dressed the financial elite of New York and later the entire United States. Gustave Fabergé had been a jeweller in Saint-Petersburg since 1842, but his son Peter-Karl made the house famous as a purveyor to the Russian Tsar Nicolaus II (Cat. 60). And there were many others, like Garrard since 1792, Hankock's since 1849 in London, and Köchert since 1807 in Vienna.

The Belle Epoque came at a time of international tension, the formation of blocks of power in politics, which regrettably would result in the First World War, 1914–1918. Because of the system of constitutional monarchies many monarchs were less interested in ruling than before, so they sought diversion in 'gay Paris', together with the owners and the fils à papa of the great industrial fortunes. The nightlife flourished, opera and cabaret on every corner. Because of the deemed inexhaustible supply of African diamond reserves, corsages, brooches, necklaces and diadems took on immense proportions. On stage, actresses wore conspicuous jewels that could be seen at the back of the theatre, giving the wealthy women in the audience expensive ideas. The improved methods of cutting gave jewellery even more glitter. Shortly after the end of the century, first Cartier then other jewellers started using platinum as the base metal for jewels, with the advantage that it didn't discolour like silver, and that it could be used in such a way one could barely see it, so the diamonds seemed to 'float' (*Cat. 57, 60*).

Another diamond style of the time was the garland style, named after the designs of the Cartier house. It was extremely successful and taken up by other jewellers. Sometimes one speaks of jewels from that period as the Edwardian style, because of the flamboyant lifestyle of Edward, Prince of Wales, late crowned King Edward VII, during his many trips to the city.

The much-prized art nouveau movement, coinciding with the Belle Epoque, was not so important for diamond fanciers. The movement owes its name to Siegfried Bing's art gallery L'Art Nouveau, situated in the rue du Provence, Paris, where he exhibited Japanese and French decorative art. Art nouveau was a godsend allowing the return of the genuinely artistic jewel. Craftspeople worked closely with artists, especially poets and painters. The new trends had a negative effect on diamond use. Very few great diamond jewels were produced in the art nouveau style. Diamond is seen here and there, as a small but important touch.

The twentieth century

After the First World War, Antwerp became for the second time, after the sixteenth century, the world centre for diamond trade and processing. With the art deco movement, a massive amount of diamonds began to be used again. New diamond mines were discovered in Africa, specifically in the colony of the Belgian Congo. At the same time, the Soviets threw the enormous stash of diamonds belonging to the murdered Russian tsar's family onto the market. In 1927, a huge auction of the jewellery and loose diamonds of the Romanovs was held at Christie's in London. With the war, new and huge fortunes had formed, and the newly acquired

freedom allowed these riches to be fully enjoyed. The art deco period also revealed new cuts, which still exist now: the baguette, the triangle, the square cut, the lozenge and the trapeze have all contributed to giving jewels with nothing but diamonds some variation and structure (*Cat. 65, 66*).

After the Second World War and the recovery of the economy, pre-war trends were revived. But times had changed for jewellery production. Right beside haute couture jewellery stood the trinkets, often in man-made material, which are part of the youth experience, rebellion, the mods and rockers, punks, hippies, hell's angels, and so on. The influence of America and its consumer goods was inevitable. The old 'good taste' criteria were severely challenged, as the globalisation of fashion and the suburban subculture grew. Today, the younger generations no longer imitate movie divas like Audrey Hepburn, Brigitte Bardot or Elizabeth Taylor, who dressed in 'real' clothes and 'real' jewellery. The teens and twenty-somethings have their own icons, they want to dress casually and look like Jennifer Lopez, Britney Spears, David Beckham, queens and kings of pop music and sports. Some jewellery houses have produced very expensive jewellery to reflect these changing tastes of the young (*Cat. 138, 139*).

Another modern influence on jewellery happened after 1960, where jewellery was, like ceramics, glass and textiles, seen as an art form. The diamond industry, to keep abreast of these changes, now makes an effort to attract artists for diamond jewels through competitions. The Diamond Trading Company has historically held a global design competition, the Diamonds International Awards, and still encourages young designers through frequent design programmes worldwide. In Antwerp the biannual HRD-Awards (Diamond High Council) are now open to designers across the world. These initiatives, which are held to inspire designers, have sometimes unusual results, with diamonds being used alongside novel materials such as rubber, wood, plastics and even coal (*Cat. 125, 152, 156*). The diamond industry has followed suit by creating

This platinum-and-coal necklace designed by Cornelia Rating is set with 1528 black and white diamonds weighing 71.8 carats (*Cat. 155*).

new cuts, often considered more 'trendy' than the centuries-old brilliant. As they have fewer facets to be polished, and can keep more weight than the brilliant, new cuts are even more profitable for the diamond market (*Cat. 132, 133, 142*).

The great jewellery houses still produce expensive pieces for high society, usually with a careful glance at the new trends. At times one sees a new house. The fashion queen Coco Chanel designed a jewellery series in 1932 that was so successful it now has a jewellery department. It is a trend indeed that famous companies, in the beginning specialised in one branch such as fashion, jewellery or perfume, now try to cover all aspects of high-quality, luxury goods.

It used to be that coloured diamonds were not always accepted, as the colour signalled a flaw of some sort. Nowadays coloured diamonds are prized, and some jewellery artists are specialised in the use of them. Many others find inspiration in the exotic, originating from the growth of tourism and knowledge of far-flung places or topical issues. The series of Panther jewellery by Cartier certainly has to do with the world's growing concern for the conservation of endangered wildlife (*Cat. 148*).

The more expensive a jewel, the more exclusive and personal it appears. The most expensive jewellery and the largest diamonds often receive the name of a famous owner, like the Empress Josephine tiara, the Empress Marie-Louise necklace, the Regent, the Sancy, the Hope diamond. They are all signs of the power of diamond, this spectacular stone that keeps the world enthralled and the beauty of which is a true phenomenon. But the sensationalism that sometimes surrounds diamonds will, however, never threaten the intimate magic of the stone that keeps everyone, young and old, rich and poor, in its spell.

Jan Walgrave
Honorary Director of the Antwerp Province Museums

The technology of diamond

The use of diamond in technology reflects the unique combination of its extreme properties, not just the fact it is the hardest known substance. Diamond conducts heat readily, expands and contracts little with changing temperature, transmits light and other electromagnetic radiation with great efficiency, and is resistant to a wide variety of chemicals. Any one of these properties would make diamond a valuable material, but together they mean diamond has some unique technical uses.

Diamond has fascinated technologists since before 1797 when the English chemist Simon Tennant showed conclusively that diamond consists of pure carbon. From early in the nineteenth century, attempts were made to make diamond in the laboratory. At first these were driven by scientific curiosity, but later, as the combination of properties possessed by diamond was recognised, industrial need became the incentive.

Early experiments were hazardous. James Hannay, a Scottish chemist, regularly reduced his laboratory to ruins as he tried to generate the high pressures needed to form diamond. Eventually he found some tiny diamonds in one of his experimental runs and, in 1880, claimed to have synthesised diamond. Nearly a century later, however, in 1962 Hannay's diamonds were shown to be natural stones. Possibly a sense of self-preservation led one of Hannay's employees to plant the diamonds to put an end to his explosive experiments.

Other attempts also ended in self-delusion. The French chemist Henri Moissan died in 1907 believing he had synthesised diamond. Later work suggested he had only made carborundum (silicon carbide), now often used as an abrasive.

During the twentieth century, individual researchers continued the quest, but it was only in the 1940s industry began developing safe, high-pressure apparatus. Two companies made the breakthrough simultaneously. Late in 1954, scientists at General Electric in the USA were able to show in a series of repeatable experiments that they could synthesise diamond. The previous year, a Swedish company ASEA, had achieved the same feat but made no announcement until after General Electric published its success in 1955.

Both companies relied on apparatus that could generate immense pressure while allowing the starting materials to be heated. The General Electric experiments were run at 100,000 atmospheres and 1600°C. What proved critical was to have a metal such as iron present in the apparatus as well as carbon. Subsequent experience showed the metal needed to melt and dissolve the carbon just as the pressure and temperature reached levels under which diamond is stable. With its first patent, General Electric claimed diamond could be synthesised from any carbon-rich material. To justify the claim, its scientists made diamond from a wide range of substances including crunchy peanut butter.

High-pressure, high-temperature processes for making diamond, like those pioneered by General Electric and ASEA, became established on an industrial scale in the early 1960s. Synthesis by explosive shock was also developed by some companies. Together these processes are used to provide large quantities of small diamonds for industrial use.

Another process called Chemical Vapour Deposition (CVD), developed in the mid 1980s, has opened up new ways in which diamond can be used in industry. The process does not rely on high pressures but on high temperatures of over 2000°C, which are used to react a gas mixture containing methane. The process 'fools' the carbon present to deposit as small crystals of diamond rather than as graphite, which would be the most stable form of carbon at low pressures. The resulting diamond, usually deposited as a thin wafer on silicon, consists of a dense mass of small crystals fused together to make a continuous sheet. The particular benefits of the CVD process are that it provides diamond that can be grown to some size and made to a specified purity.

The hardness and resistance to wear of diamond means it has found many uses in abrasive and cutting tools, from oilfield drilling bits and saws for stone, to manufacturing machinery and polishing pastes. Diamond is routinely manufactured and used for such purposes along with the 80% of diamonds mined each year that are not of gem quality. Some fine diamonds are sintered together with cobalt to give polycrystalline diamond (PCD), a material tougher than single diamond crystals, which can be brittle and cleave. PCD is mainly used for cutting non-ferrous metals and alloys, fine-machining wood composites such as MDF and protecting surfaces that suffer major wear.

Thin wafers of CVD diamond can be fashioned for use. For instance, ultra-sharp, extremely thin blades can be made for surgical and laboratory instruments. One such device, which is used for cutting very thin slices of organic tissue for examination in an electron microscope, could divide the thickness of a banknote into 4000 slices.

Diamond's combination of properties is exploited in other ways. For instance, it is an ideal material for windows behind which sensitive monitoring equipment can be housed. The Venus space probe used a natural diamond measuring 18.2 millimetres in diameter and 2.8 millimetres thick as a window for some of its apparatus to operate through. However, natural diamonds of this size are very expensive and often do not have the purity needed for technical use. CVD diamond can provide a suitable alternative material when carefully manufactured to provide the necessary optical properties and strength. CVD diamond windows are used in applications ranging from large-scale chemical manufacturing plants to high-power lasers and on guided missiles.

Diamonds can be used to subject small samples to extreme pressures in laboratory apparatus called a diamond anvil cell. Pressure applied to the broad end of two or more diamond crystals is used to exert much larger pressures on samples held between the points of the diamonds, which have smaller surface areas. The ability of the diamonds to transmit heat and radiation allows the sample to be heated and studied while the experiment is carried out. Conditions deep in the Earth, for example, can be simulated in this way.

Electronics is another area of actual and potential application. Diamond, rather than copper, is already used to conduct heat away from key components in some lasers. In the future, the emerging role of diamond as a semiconductor may also take off. This will require finding efficient ways of 'doping' diamond with elements such as boron, which turn it from being an electrical insulator to a semiconductor.

Looking to the future, high-quality mined diamonds will continue to provide rare gems for jewellery, whether for engagement rings or for rich extravagance. Most mined diamonds, though, and a range of synthesised diamond, are likely to find increasing use in industry and science for tackling a host of technical problems.

Andrew Fleet
Mineralogy Department, Natural History Museum

1 The Steinmetz Pink

59.60 carats
Fancy vivid pink oval-shaped mixed cut
Southern Africa

Pink diamonds have been known for hundreds of years, but a vivid pink diamond of such size, clarity and saturated colour is almost unprecedented. It was cut from a rough crystal of 132.50 carats, following two years of intensive study and planning by the Steinmetz Diamond Group, and was first shown in Monaco, May 2003. It is internally flawless.

THE STEINMETZ DIAMOND GROUP

2 The Heart of Eternity

27.64 carats
Fancy vivid blue heart-shaped modified brilliant
South Africa

Natural blue diamonds are very rare, a large diamond of such a vivid blue astonishingly so. This stunning gem was the centrepiece of a collection of 11 blue diamonds unveiled by De Beers for the Millennium celebrations. They came from South Africa's Premier Mine, a well-known source of blue diamonds of varying intensity and size. The colour is due to the presence of tiny amounts of boron.

PRIVATE COLLECTION

3 The Moussaieff Red

5.11 carats
Fancy red modified triangular brilliant
Brazil

Even at just over five carats, this is an astounding size for a natural red diamond – very few diamonds indeed are described as 'red'. It is so rare that the Gemological Institute of America, in authenticating it as naturally coloured, claimed never to have graded such a diamond before. It was cut from a 13.90-carat crystal found by a Brazilian farmer in the mid 1990s.

MOUSSAIEFF JEWELLERS/SMITHSONIAN INSTITUTION, WASHINGTON DC

4 The Ocean Dream

5.51 carats
Fancy deep blue-green modified triangular brilliant
Central Africa

The deep blue-green colour of this diamond is extraordinarily rare. In nature, only exposure to high-energy radiation over a long period of time – thousands or even millions of years – results in such a saturated green throughout the whole crystal. The 11.27-carat rough from which it came was subject to intense study and testing during the process of cutting, between 2002 and 2003, to confirm the colour is indeed natural.

CORA DIAMOND CORPORATION, NEW YORK

5 The Orange Flame
3.23 carats
South Africa?

This wonderfully vivid gem is, in the eyes of diamond experts, one of the most beautiful orange diamonds you will ever see. The intensity and purity of its colour, with the slightest hint of yellow, is remarkable. Nature rarely produces orange diamonds of this size and calibre. Most are below one carat in weight, and exhibit either a strong brownish or strong yellowish tone.

PRIVATE COLLECTION

6 The Incomparable Diamond
407.48 carats
Fancy brownish-yellow kite shape
Democratic Republic of Congo

This internally flawless, fancy brownish-yellow diamond is the third largest cut diamond ever recorded. It was the largest of 15 gems cut from an 890-carat rough found in the early 1980s by a young girl playing in waste rubble from a diamond mine in the Mbuji-Mayi district of the Democratic Republic of Congo. Four years of study and cutting resulted in this unusual 'kite' shape. At first, the cutter's hope was to break the record for the largest diamond in the world, but in the end, size was sacrificed for perfect clarity – making it the largest flawless diamond ever cut.

ZALE CORPORATION, DALLAS, TEXAS;
MARVIN SAMUELS, PREMIER GEM CORPORATION, NEW YORK;
LOUIS GLICK, LOUIS GLICK & COMPANY, NEW YORK

7 The 616
616 carats
Uncut octahedral crystal
South Africa

This 616 carat crystal, as found and remaining uncut, is the largest single diamond crystal in the world, greater in carat weight than any cut diamond known today. It comes from the Dutoitspan Mine in Kimberley, South Africa, focus of the late 19th-century diamond rush.

DE BEERS CONSOLIDATED MINES (ON LOAN UNTIL 6 DEC.)

8 The Allnatt
101.29 carats, brooch diamonds and platinum
Fancy vivid yellow round-cornered square cut
South Africa?

This is one of the largest naturally vivid yellow diamonds in the world. Although its origins are not certain, it is typical of the intensely yellow stones from the De Beers Mine in South Africa during the early years of production. It is named after a previous owner, Major Alfred Ernest Allnatt, a British soldier, art patron and philanthropist, who purchased it in the 1950s. He commissioned Cartier to design a floral brooch setting for it.
It was later recut to intensify the colour further.

SIBA CORP. OF NEW YORK (ON LOAN UNTIL 20 SEPT.)

9 The De Beers Millennium Star

203.04 carats
Flawless D colour pear shape
Democratic Republic of Congo

This remarkable pear-shaped gem was cut from a rough diamond of 777 carats, the sixth largest 'colourless' gem-quality diamond ever found. The rough was plucked from river gravel diggings in the district of Mbuji-Mayi in the Democratic Republic of Congo in the early 1990s. De Beers purchased it, and after three years of study, planning and work by the Steinmetz Diamond Group, the rough was divided into three parts. This the largest gem, of dazzling brilliance, was unveiled in late 1999 as the centrepiece of a unique exhibition at the Millennium Dome in London. It became the target of an audacious, and fortunately foiled, robbery attempt in 2000.

DE BEERS LV, 50 OLD BOND STREET

10 The Banjarmasin diamond
38.22 carats
White, cushion cut
Borneo

This is the largest diamond ever known from Borneo, a small but significant source of diamonds for hundreds of years. It is said to have been cut from an almost perfect octahedral crystal weighing more than 70 carats, which is known to have belonged to the Sultan of Banjarmasin (a kingdom on the island) in 1836. There are no records to indicate when this diamond became part of his treasury. It was taken to the Netherlands when the sultanate became a Dutch colony in 1859, and was cut between 1870 and 1880 by order of the Dutch government into this cushion-cut gem, losing 40% of its weight in the process. It was eventually given to the Rijksmuseum in Amsterdam.

RIJKSMUSEUM, AMSTERDAM

14 'The Six Voyages of Jean-Baptiste Tavernier'
English translation, London, 1677–78
French writer, traveller and trade merchant, Jean-Baptiste

Tavernier amassed a small fortune through his expertise and trade in diamonds and precious stones. During his travels to Turkey, Persia, India and other countries of southeast Asia, he befriended many of the greatest Oriental potentates and was privileged to inspect the treasuries of the Grand Mogul. He was also one of the few westerners ever to gain access to the fabled Indian diamond mines. Tavernier recounted his journeys in his publication *Les Six Voyages de J B Tavernier* (2 vol, Paris, 1676), which included accounts of Japan and Tonkin. This edition was translated by J Phillips and published in London, 1678.

NATURAL HISTORY MUSEUM LIBRARY

15 The Shah Jahan diamond
56.7 carats
H 33, W 46, D 3 mm
India

An historic and extraordinary, very pale pink diamond, the octagonal table-cut Shah Jahan has been known since at least the early 17th century. One side has small drill holes where the diamond could be sewn into clothing or attached to jewellery. Careful inspection reveals marks of earlier, more widely spaced holes, indicating it may have fractured during an earlier attempt to cut it. This means the diamond may have originally weighed more than it does today. It has been confirmed by experts to be the one mounted in the turban ornament held by Shah Jahan in the 1616 miniature.

THE AL-SABAH COLLECTION, DAR AL-ALTHAR
AL-ISLAMIYYAH, KUWAIT, LNS 2156 J

16 Portrait of Shah Jahan as a prince
Gouache and gold on paper
Mogul manuscript, Nadir al-Zamin, c. 1616–17
Miniature
206 x 115 mm, page 390 x 267 mm

A miniature portrait of Prince Khurram, the future Emperor Shah Jahan. He is pictured holding a golden turban ornament set with a cushion-shaped emerald and large octagonal diamond. Study of the contours and size of the stone has shown this is unquestionably the Shah Jahan diamond. A later inscription by Shah Jahan on the border reads, 'A good likeness of me in my twenty-fifth year and the fine work of Nadir al-Zamin'.

VICTORIA AND ALBERT MUSEUM, INV. 14–1925

18 The Spanish Inquisition Necklace
Diamond, emerald, platinum
Provenance unknown, part 17th century

Composed of two strands of antique-cut diamonds and emeralds, to which a lower pendant and upper chain containing modern, brilliant-cut diamonds has been added, the necklace holds a total of 374 diamonds. The 16 large barrel-shaped diamonds in this elegant necklace were probably cut in India in the 17th century. Mounted in a most extraordinary way, each has two angled drill holes on one side that connect within the stone. A wire passing through the resulting V-shape channel almost invisibly secures the stone to the necklace. Little is known about the history of the necklace, but according to legend, at least a portion, or variation, of it was once the property of Spanish royalty and later adorned ladies of the French court. The origin of the name remains a mystery.

NATIONAL MUSEUM OF NATURAL HISTORY, SMITHSONIAN INSTITUTION, WASHINGTON DC (ON LOAN UNTIL 6 DEC.)

19 Indian diamond and enamel necklace
Gold, diamonds, enamel, L 457 mm
c. 1850

A dense pattern of table-cut diamonds form a scrolled floral motif, with a suspended courting peacock in diamond, and a smaller pendant beneath. On the reverse is red, blue and green enamel. The necklace has an adjustable back string.

PRIVATE COLLECTION

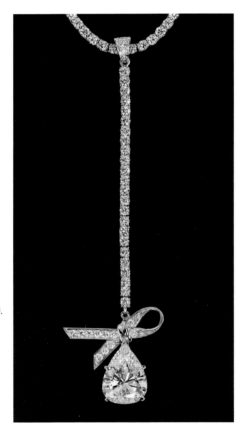

23 Golconda diamond necklace
Diamonds, platinum
Bruce Oldfield for Cool Diamonds, 2005

This necklace, designed by Bruce Oldfield, showcases a rare 10.63-carat pear-shaped Golconda diamond, which dates back to 1940. Golconda diamonds, named after the ancient city at the heart of India's diamond trade, are world-famous for their ultra-transparency. The twisted ribbon motif, now often associated with charities for AIDS and breast cancer, was chosen because 'it has a generic feel-good element'.

COOL DIAMONDS, LONDON

20 Elephant goad (*ankus*)
Gold, set with diamonds on blue, green or red enamel, with polychrome painted enamel on grip. L 545 mm
Jaipur, *c.* 1870

This elaborately ornamented goad, with scenes of the hunt on the grip, was made for ceremonial purposes. It was acquired by the India Museum after being shown in the 1871 Exhibition.

VICTORIA AND ALBERT MUSEUM,
INV. 02963 (IS)

25 Reliquary cross pendant

Gold, diamonds, pearls, enamel, cross with pearl,
89 x 62 mm, connecting chain L 45 mm
Germany? partly end of 16th century,
partly *c.* 1620

The arms of the cross are decorated with five
high-set cases, within each of which are two
table-cut diamonds. Between them is an
unusual diagonal cross form, low set with one
table-cut and three nine-faceted diamonds.
Hanging pearls finish this remarkable jewel.
The chain appears to be partly original, with
seven baroque pearls, and four hearts and four
letters H with traces of enamel.

The relic would have been placed beneath the
highly decorated cover on the reverse side.
The multi-coloured enamel scrollwork, featuring
satyrs, dolphins, dragonflies and the like, is
reminiscent of the ornamental prints of an
Antwerp designer Adriaen Collaert (d. 1618).

PRIVATE COLLECTION, BELGIUM

24 Pendant with Jesus monogram

Gold, diamonds, enamel, 39 x 29 mm
Northern Europe, *c.* 1550

Twenty-six angular, table-cut diamonds form
the overlapping letters IHS (Iesus Hominis
Salvator – Jesus, Saviour of Man).
The S loops between the other two letters, and
the I rises up to form part of a cross. The
diamonds are of a high quality for this period,
except for two yellow stones.

IHS pendants are traditional devotional jewels,
valued as talismans and heirlooms. They first
appeared in the second half of the 15th century
and can be difficult to date. They often occur in
paintings of the period, for example in the
portrait of Jane Seymour, third wife of Henry
VIII of England, by Hans Holbein (1536–37),
now in the Kunsthistorisches Museum in Vienna.

**VICTORIA AND ALBERT MUSEUM, GIFT OF
DAME JOAN EVANS, INV. M. 76–1975**

27 Pendant in the form of a lizard

Gold, diamonds, rubies, enamel, 67 x 21 mm,
with chain H 56 mm
Spain? *c.* 1600

A table-cut diamond and two lozenge-shaped
rubies are set on the lizard's thin, flat body, with
smaller diamonds in between and on the elbows
of the four legs. Small point-cut stones form its
eyes and the long tail has 10 table-cut
diamonds – this row arrangement is typical of
the early 17th century. The body is coated
above and below with pale green enamel, with
a black scaled design, which gives it a very
naturalistic appearance, especially on the
underside. The Moroccan rock lizard (*Lacerta
perspicillata*), also found in Spain, may have
served as a model.

PRIVATE COLLECTION, BELGIUM

28 Peapod corsage brooch

Gold, diamonds, enamel, 126 x 73 mm
France or the Netherlands, *c*. 1630

The stylised floral brooch is a fine example of a cosse-de-pois
or peapod-style bodice ornament fashionable in the 1620s and
1630s, and shows the emerging dominance of diamond over
sculpted and enamelled gold. Peapod-like arches swirl around a
rosette that has a central table-cut diamond surrounded by four
similar diamonds. The whole jewel is covered with diamonds and
some white enamel grains. The design is inspired by the drawings
of French jeweller Balthasar Lemercier, who published his
drawings in 1626 in Paris.

**VICTORIA AND ALBERT MUSEUM,
GIFT OF DAME JOAN EVANS, INV. M. 143–1975**

30 Girandole parure

Silver, rose-cut diamonds, brooch 60 x 70 mm,
eardrops 44 x 39 mm
Probably Spain, 18th century

Both brooch and eardrops (which have been subsequently
changed into brooches) are extended widthways with elaborate
ribbon and vine elements. They are completely covered with flat
rose-cut diamonds, a type known as Antwerp roses. Each part of
the jewel has a larger rose diamond in the centre and three
pendants with a loose teardrop attached to them. This design is
called a *girandole*, named after a type of ornamental branched
candleholder, sometimes backed by a mirror. The term parure
means a matching set of jewellery.

PRIVATE COLLECTION, BELGIUM

31 Bow stomacher

Gold, silver, diamonds, 214 x 125 mm
Dresden, Christian August Globig, 1782

This beautiful jewel was given by Frederik August III to his wife, Amalia-Augusta von Pfalz-Zweibrücken in 1782, on the occasion of the birth of their daughter Maria-Augusta. The double bow has two rows of lightly waving, broad ribbons, each with larger diamonds flanked by a row of smaller ones. Between the rows lies a zigzag line of smaller stones, which subtly lightens this imposing jewel. The largest stone stands centrally as the knot, surrounded by 15 smaller stones. At the sides, more diamonds run through to the back, creating a relief. Underneath, two end-pieces have been applied. The closed back is strengthened and has two clasps for fastening the jewel to the bodice.

The combined weight of the 662 brilliants is an estimated 614 carats. In order to compose it, Globig had to dismantle a number of other jewels: 27 coat buttons and 12 vest buttons, two epaulettes and an insignia of the Polish Order of the White Eagle. The large stone in the middle is taken from an ornamental button on a shirt.

This corsage bow is the largest preserved from the 18th century, except for the 250 mm bow of Tsarina Catharina II of Russia, which is in the Gochran Foundation, Kremlin, Moscow.

STAATLICHE KUNSTSAMMLUNGEN, GRÜNES GEWÖLBE, DRESDEN, GERMANY, INV. VII 36 (ON LOAN UNTIL 6 DEC.)

34 Two shoe buckles

Silver, silver gilt, steel, brilliants, 57 x 84 x 38 mm
Dresden, Christian August Globig, 1782–89

The open buckles are decorated with a total of 64 larger diamonds, surrounded by 181 smaller ones. They form part of the Brilliant Garnitur, or costume jewel set, of Augustus the Strong (1670–1733), Prince-elector of Saxony and, as August II, King of Poland.

STAATLICHE KUNSTSAMMLUNGEN, GRÜNES GEWÖLBE, DRESDEN, GERMANY, INV. VIII 19 (ON LOAN UNTIL 6 DEC.)

40 Aigrette

Silver, diamonds, 112 x 70 mm
England? *c.* 1780

The plumes in this aigrette are completely studded with small rose-cut diamonds mounted on foil in a closed silver setting. The name aigrette comes from the French for 'little egret'. Fine, ornamental plumes from the bird's head were placed in a holder to be worn as a jewel in the hair and, from the 18th century onwards, also on a corsage. These plumes were imitated using precious metals and stones, more durable than the extremely valuable but more perishable plumage. Designs could be very elaborate, such as those of the French jeweller Pouget. In England, people were less enthusiastic about the exuberant rococo style popular on the continent, and English jewellery gives a somewhat stiffer impression.

DIAMOND MUSEUM, PROVINCE OF ANTWERP, BELGIUM, INV. DMK 02/2

41 Necklace of rosettes and small sprays

Gold, silver, diamonds, 465 x 27 mm
Netherlands? Mid 18th century

This is a simple but particularly well-rendered jewel, set with rose-cut diamonds of uneven colour, although quite skilfully cut. The seven rosettes alternate with eight sprays, with a five-petal flower on each branch. The rosettes consist of five octagonal links with a rose-cut diamond at the centre, as is the rosette fastening. All the stones are in closed mountings.

PRIVATE COLLECTION, BELGIUM

44 Garter Star
Gold, silver, diamonds, rubies, enamel, 150 x 150 mm
England? end of 17th century? altered in 1858

The Most Noble Order of the Garter, founded in 1348 by Edward III, is the oldest and highest order of chivalry of the kingdom. The exact original composition of this large Garter Star is uncertain, since it was remade in 1858. It was probably made for Queen Anne as a gift for her husband Prince George of Denmark, whom she married in 1683, but who apparently never wore it. King George III did, from 1788. In 1858 it was altered for Queen Victoria, to wear on her Garter mantle.

The centre cross is made of 13 rubies, surrounded by diamonds in gold, and encircled by the Garter in blue enamel. In 1858, the centre was remade with 18 brilliants, the Garter motto was re-set with rose cuts, and an original two-carat drop brilliant was replaced, as well as many other stones. The rays have been fixed and reinforced with gold.

HER MAJESTY THE QUEEN, INV. RCIN 441147

46 Order of the Garter Badge (Great George)
Gold, silver, diamonds, sapphires, rubies, amethysts,
150 x 67 x 35 mm
Probably partly English, partly Viennese, 1780–1800

The whole statuette is lavishly covered with diamonds, some details accentuated with other gemstones. It appears for the first time in an inventory of 1819, but must have been made earlier, since there are clear references to it in correspondence concerning King George III. The fleur-de-lys suspension, although supposed to have been added later, echoes the style of earlier Great Georges. The fact it is rather large and has a base for standing upright is, however, no reason to consider it was meant as an *objet de vertu* rather than a badge to be worn. There are larger Georges with a base, like the one made by Dillinger for the Prince Elector Johann Georg IV in Dresden, 1692–94 (Grünes Gewölbe, inv. VIII 266).

HER MAJESTY THE QUEEN, INV. RCIN 441144

48 The Murchison snuff box
Gold, diamonds and enamel
Russia, 1867

A rectangular gold and diamond snuff box with a portrait of
Alexander II, Emperor of Russia, on enamel, signed Rockstuhl.
The portrait is surrounded by 16 large, old brilliant-cut diamonds
in a design of foliage set with rose-cut diamonds. The larger
stones range in size from 5.5 to 9 mm diameter and in weight
from 0.75 to 2.5 carats. The box was a present from the Emperor
to Sir Roderick Murchison in recognition of his geological
explorations in Russia. It is engraved inside 'Presented by His
Imperial Majesty Alexander the 2nd, Emperor of all of Russia, to
Sir Roderick Impey Murchison Bart, Director General of the
Geological Survey, Explorer of Russia and the Ural Mountains, 1867'.

**NATURAL HISTORY MUSEUM, MINERALOGY DEPARTMENT:
NHM 1935, 1219**

49 Original plaster cast of Koh-i-Noor before recutting
England, 1851

These plaster casts are of immense historical importance, as they
represent the original form of arguably the world's most famous
diamond, which now in its recut form is part of the British Crown
Jewels. The Koh-i-Noor had been demanded in tribute from the
Sikhs in 1849, at the end of the Sikh wars, and arrived in London
set in an armlet, with two smaller diamonds.

The great diamond was, to European eyes, not brilliant enough,
and a decision was made to recut it. These models were prepared
before the recutting, during April 1851 by Mr Pink of the British
Museum, with Messrs Garrard in attendance to detach the gems
from their original armlet and weigh them. The Koh-i-Noor
plaster cast is marked on the underside in pencil: 'The original
cast from the Koh-i-Noor before it was recut, 1851' and signed
NSM (Nevil Story-Maskelyne, Keeper of Mineralogy). The two
smaller casts are of the two additional stones.

**NATURAL HISTORY MUSEUM, MINERALOGY DEPARTMENT:
KOH-I-NOOR CAST, NHM 85480; TWO PENDANTS, NHM 85481**

51 The Thurn und Taxis four rivières necklace
Gold, silver, diamonds
Western Europe, c. 1840

Four rivières (meaning 'rivers') is set with cushion-shaped brilliants, lined up *en chute*: gradated from the largest at the front to the smallest behind. This remarkable jewel is from the Thurn und Taxis family, originally from Bergamo in Italy. For more than 300 years, they held the monopoly over imperial communications and post between Vienna and the far flung Holy Roman Empire, under the patronage of the Hapsburgs. Thanks to the imperial monopoly, their business grew to be an enormous firm. They only lost their monopoly with the end of the Holy Roman Empire in 1804. But by then their wealth and position was assured.

The quadruple rivières is especially remarkable because, at the time it was made, diamond supplies were dwindling, due to the exhaustion of the Brazilian mines. It would have been almost impossible to compose a collection of such high-quality stones, with the exact carat gradation needed for the *en chute* positioning. It must have taken years to collect all the right gems.

PRIVATE COLLECTION

52 Wreath tiara or necklace
Gold, silver, diamonds, rubies, 180 x 185 mm
Western Europe, c. 1835

A tiara in the shape of a flower wreath, set in silver and riveted to a golden frame: on the front are three climbing roses with two larger lilies in between, and towards the back some forget-me-nots. The lilies have a golden stamen with a ruby at the top. The fastening allowing this tiara to be worn also as a necklace is missing. Few of these sumptuous jewels have survived, as they were very often divided into smaller sprays by following generations.

This is a fine example of a tiara that would have been given to a bride as part of her *corbeille de noces*: a crown of symbolic meanings. According to Pratt and Miller, forget-me-nots stand for expectant love; the lily is a Christian symbol for purity beliefs and also represent sweetness and enduring beauty. Wild roses stand for spontaneous love, an optimistic thought indeed in a time when marriages were almost always arranged by the parents.

VICTORIA AND ALBERT MUSEUM, INV. M. 45-1980

53 Golden spray brooch with a larger and a smaller flower
Gold, diamonds, 78 x 55 mm
Country? *c.* 1850

A larger flower with irregular petals almost fills the surface of this jewel, which is entirely mounted in gold. All stones are rose-cuts, in open mountings made by perforating the gold.

MRS J. ZEBERG COLLECTION, ANTWERP

54 Branch brooch with an eglantine *en tremblant*
Gold, silver, diamonds, 108 x 63 mm
Probably England, *c.* 1860

A branch with an open and a closed eglantine, or wild rose, *en tremblant*. The rose-cut diamonds are in open mountings, except for the central rose-cut diamond in the flower. A golden hook at the back reveals this elegant branch was once part of a larger whole.

MRS J. ZEBERG COLLECTION, ANTWERP

55 Spray brooch with a flower
Gold, silver, diamonds, 87 x 38 mm
Country? *c.* 1880

An almost straight twig carries a five-petal flower to one side, held on a worn trembling rod. At its centre is an old brilliant-cut diamond, surrounded by golden stamens tipped with diamonds. Foliage and a few buds, strewn with rose-cut diamonds, complete this elegant little jewel.

MRS J. ZEBERG COLLECTION, ANTWERP

57 *Devant de corsage* or bodice ornament of two lily sprays
Platinum, diamonds, L 273 mm each branch
Cartier, Paris, 1906

Corsage jewel in garland style with 2339 diamonds in mille-grain setting, partly old brilliant and partly rose cut. It has a very flexible frame, enabling the jewel to adapt to the wearer. The two lily sprays, entwined by eglantine (wild rose), are joined by a hinge covered with a larger brilliant, so the jewel's width could be adjusted.

The 18th century was the great age for bodice jewellery: the dress bodice was flattened and a stiff triangle of jewellery or heavy embroidery was applied, often with floral inspiration. Around 1900, the corsage adornment was again much *en vogue*, but women no longer wore rigid whalebone corsets, and the flexibility of larger jewellery pieces was popular.

The Cartier House indulged the more traditional tastes of its high society clientele. Such flower designs were in the naturalistic style promoted by Empress Eugénie of France in the earlier 19th century, in turn inspired by the 18th-century 'Marie-Antoinette' style. This piece was made as a special order for Mary Scott Townsend, an eminent member of Washington's high society, and her great niece Thora Ronalds McElroy, heir to the Scott-Strong coal and railroad fortune.

CARTIER COLLECTION

58 The Eureka
10.73 carats
Southern Africa

Despite this diamond's distinct yellow coloration and many imperfections and inclusions, it is of extraordinary historical importance. It is the first officially recorded diamond on the African continent, cut from a 21.25-carat rough found in late 1866 in cemented gravels of a river terrace on the bank of the Orange River. Although several different versions of the discovery exist, it is believed the finder of the diamond was Erasmus Jacobs, the fifteen-year-old son of a Boer farmer, and it was for a while just a shiny keepsake. It was later identified as a diamond by Dr W. G. Atherstone of Grahamstown, one of the few people in the Cape Colony with knowledge of minerals and gems.

THE GOVERNMENT OF THE REPUBLIC OF SOUTH AFRICA (ON LOAN UNTIL 6 DEC.)

59 The Star of South Africa
47.69 carats
Southern Africa
(Pendant, Cartier, New York, 1910s)

Discovered in 1869, close to where the Orange and Vaal rivers converge, the original 83.50-carat crystal was later cut into a gem, to be named the Star of South Africa. The Griqua shepherd who discovered the stone was traded 500 sheep, 10 head of cattle and one horse for his find. The discovery was to attract thousands of people to the region and so start the South African diamond rush. Shown here suspended from a detachable pendant designed by Cartier, this flawless pear-shaped diamond is regarded as the symbol of South Africa's mineral development.

PRIVATE COLLECTION

60 Fabergé tiara

Gold, platinum, brilliant- and rose-cut diamonds,
H 130 mm, W 250 mm
St-Petersburg, Albert Holström studio for Fabergé, 1903

This diadem in the 'kokoshnik' style (a stiff halo in the form of a traditional Russian headdress) is composed as a tracery of knife-like wires, creating a delicate openwork. Small stylised forget-me-not flowers are placed at the intersections, and there are trails of laurels around the edges. It is a magnificent example of the then-new possibilities of platinum: a far stronger metal than either gold or silver, which could therefore be used very sparingly. Here, the fine knife-wire with its sharp edges reflects a thin line of bright light and suggests an almost invisible setting. The piece is unmarked but undoubtedly from the workshop of chief jewellery workmaster Holmström.

PRIVATE COLLECTION

64 Sunburst tiara

Platinum, diamonds, sapphire
Cartier, Paris, 1921

The tiara, designed to be worn low on the forehead, is composed of platinum rays with 577 brilliants and several rose-cut diamonds, meeting in a centre, where originally a jonquil coloured, 71-carat diamond was set like a sun. The diamond was later replaced by a large star sapphire. The central element is mounted *en tremblant*, responding to the wearer's every move.

This jewel is remarkable because of the virtuoso mille-grain settings of brilliants alternating with rose-cut diamonds. It was made for the Tyszkiewicz family and completed in August 1921.

PRIVATE COLLECTION

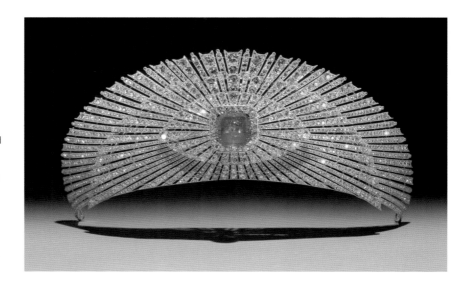

62 Diamond corsage ornament

Gold, silver, diamonds, L 143 mm
France, mid 19th century

A corsage jewel in the form of a rose branch, *pavé*-set with old European-cut diamonds, with a blooming rose surrounded by rosebuds and leaves. It is in the style of the Second Empire (1852–70) of Emperor Napoleon III and Empress Eugénie of France. The master jeweller O. Massin laid down the prototype of the famous rose branch brooches, and they remained popular for the rest of the century.

The brooch comes from the estate of the daughter of Napoleon's brother Jerome, Princess Mathilde Bonaparte, whose personal jewel collection almost equalled that of Empress Eugénie. Perhaps the rose was presented to her by the Empress. Cartier acquired it at a Paris auction of Princess Mathilde's jewellery in 1904. The same year, Cartier sold it to the wealthy Mrs Cornelius Vanderbilt (see below).

PRIVATE COLLECTION

63 Hexagonal pendant/brooch

Platinum, diamonds, H 118.5 mm, W 47 mm
Paris, Cartier, 1909

Stylised openwork motifs surround a larger brilliant. Two diamond chains lead to the matching rosette brooch, again with a larger old-cut brilliant in the middle, but in a circle of five diamonds, forming a pentagon. Underneath hang five drop diamonds. The geometrical design heralds the art deco style. Cartier made more jewels with such hexagonal forms. According to the Cartier Archives, this pendant was once part of a Renaissance-style corsage ornament composed of three identical elements, made as a special order for Mrs Cornelius Vanderbilt (1870–1953), wife of the great-grandson of US railroad magnate 'Commodore' Cornelius Vanderbilt. She was famous for her extravagant use of jewels, and a photograph shows her wearing the rose brooch, the triple pendant necklace, a large tiara and much other diamond jewellery.

CARTIER COLLECTION

68 Seven jewels to illustrate the evolution of diamond cuts

Seven gems (number 6 not shown) illustrate the gradual evolution of diamond cuts from the 4th century AD to the 20th century AD.

Stage 1: Uncut crystal *(4th century AD–16th century AD)*
1 Hand-wrought Roman ring from the late 3rd–early 4th century: represents one of the earliest known diamond rings.
2 Amber-coloured octahedral ring, 14th century

Stage 2: Table cut *(15th century onward)*
Involved breaking a diamond along a specific plane or grinding off one of its points. By the 15th century, cutters began to add more polished surfaces to increase the brilliance.
3 Antwerp-cut diamond, 1620 – the diamond is backed by silver metal foil, to help reflect light.

Stage 3: Rose cut *(late 16th–17th century and beyond)*
Facets on the domed shape of flatter crystals added brightness and created a new play of light.
4 Earrings, with diamonds mined in India set into ornate enamelled backs, Amsterdam *c.* 1660.

Stage 4: Early European brilliant cut *(late 17th century)*
Returned more light than the rose cut because of the faceting on the top and bottom, and the centralised girdle plane.
5 English ring, *c.* 1680 (a gift from Charles II to his mistress Nell Gwyn), made into a hair ornament by the Dukes of St Albans.

Stage 5: Shaped brilliant cut *(19th century)*
The outline became increasingly shaped, and a large culet (facet at the base) was cut to accentuate the gem's liveliness.
6 Two carat cushion-cut diamond given by Dom Pedro II, Emperor of Brazil (1825–91), to his niece. The vivid green diamond changes colour under different lights, which enhances its beauty *(not illustrated)*.

Stage 6: Precursor of modern brilliant cut *(early 20th century)*
Growing understanding of how faceting and proportions affect the balance of brightness, fire and scintillation, but proportions still worked out intuitively.
7 French art nouveau ring – the cut is perhaps 'clumsy' by today's standards, but many feel it has a charm missing in the modern round brilliant.

1–3, 5–7: **THE ZUCKER FAMILY COLLECTION/PRECIOUS STONES COMPANY (NEW YORK)**

4: **AS ABOVE, WITH S. J. PHILLIPS**

69 'Power of Love' ring collection

A collection of 40 diamond rings from the 8th to the late 20th century, built up by the Diamond Trading Company (DTC) to symbolise a commitment to love over the centuries. Historically, diamonds have long been symbols – or indeed talismans – of invincibility and of eternal life. Presenting a diamond ring to a beloved person signals the intention to love forever.

Beginning with ancient rings bearing hardly processed stones, the collection charts the evolution of the diamond ring in western countries, showing both the changes in fashion and the progress in working the stone: from natural octahedral and point-cut diamonds to table cuts. At the end of the 16th century came the first facetted rose-cut diamonds, and the first attempts to cut brilliants a century later. Among the rings in the collection are replicas of historically important pieces, such as the diamond betrothal ring given by Archduke Maximilian of Austria in 1477 to Mary of Burgundy. Today, the custom is as strong as ever, and through careful promotion has spread across the world.

THE DIAMOND TRADING COMPANY

72 Blue diamond solitaire
Diamond, platinum
Provenance unknown

Platinum solitaire ring with superb central, round brilliant-cut, fancy greyish blue diamond with small baguette-cut diamonds on the shoulders. The stone was probably cut in the 1920s or 1930s. The setting is unmarked.

BRITISH MUSEUM, INV. 2001, 5-5, 10

78 Portrait diamond ring
Platinum, portrait diamond, tapered baguette diamonds
Michelle Ong for Carnet, 2001

Prong-set with a portrait diamond weighing 10.53 carats, supported by a staggered stepped band of 27 tapered baguette-cut diamonds weighing 3.61 carats, mounted in platinum.

PRIVATE AMERICAN COLLECTION

81 Aurora Collection and Aurora Additions
260 fancy coloured diamonds and
36 additional gems
Total carat weight 231.73 and 35.72

This stunning collection of 296 naturally coloured diamonds has taken diamond experts Alan Bronstein and Harry Rodman over 25 years to collect. The main collection of 260 diamonds formed the centrepiece of the 1997 *Nature of Diamonds* exhibition at the American Museum of Natural History, New York. It is being exhibited for the first time in Europe, together with an additional 36 gems, collected over the past seven years, which has never before been shown in public. The diamonds range in weight from 0.13 to 2.88 carats. Many glow under ultraviolet light, as do most 'white' diamonds. Under ultraviolet light, their colour can change dramatically.

Left, Aurora Additions; below, individual stones from Aurora Additions.

ALAN BRONSTEIN AND HARRY
RODMAN/AURORA GEMS

84 Diamond in 'yellow ground'
South Africa, 1872

A fine octahedral crystal of approximately 6.5 carats embedded in 'yellow ground' from the Colesberg Kopje ('New Rush'), Griqualand West, South Africa. This surviving diamond from the very beginnings of the South African diamond mines, still encased in 'yellow ground', is extraordinarily rare. Yellow ground is the name given by early diggers working surface layers of kimberlite – the rock crumbles to this yellow clay-rich form at the surface.

NATURAL HISTORY MUSEUM, MINERALOGY DEPARTMENT:
NHM 1985, M13159

87 The Aber diamond
Diamond in matrix
Northwest Territories, Canada, 1994

The Aber diamond, estimated to weigh more than 1.76 carats, was found in a core taken from a discovery drill on the Diavik property in Canada's Northwest Territories, at the start of the Canadian diamond rush. Finding a diamond of this size in a drill sample is an extremely rare event. The discovery led to the development of the Diavik Diamond Mine, one of the world's richest ore bodies, with an estimated resource base of 119 million carats.

ABER DIAMOND COPORATION AND HARRY WINSTON

89 '**Run-of-mine**'
5000 carats (sample illustrated)
South Africa

A parcel of diamonds, known as a 'run-of-mine', shows the wide
variation in shape colour and size of natural diamonds from a
South African diamond mine. An experienced expert can tell,
from the mix of crystals, which mine it has come from. The
balance of the mix determines the profitability of the mine.
On average, only 20% of such a parcel will be classified as 'gem'
quality. Until recently, the rest would have gone to industry,
but today improved cutting techniques and changing tastes
mean that a further 30–35% may now find their way onto the
jewellery market.

THE DIAMOND TRADING COMPANY

98, 99 Cold Bokkeveld meteorite and diamond dust extracted from meteorite

Cold Bokkeveld, Cape Colony, South Africa

The Cold Bokkeveld meteorite fell to Earth on 13 October 1838 as a shower of stones. It is about 4.5 billion years old – as old as our solar system. But it contains something older still: trillions of diamonds millions of times smaller than a grain of sugar. When heated, these diamonds release minute amounts of a gas called xenon, imprisoned around the time the diamonds were formed.

Xenon occurs in a mix of different forms. The mix found in the diamonds has not been found anywhere on Earth, but is similar to our understanding of the mix in gases surrounding distant dying stars – supernovae.

The traces of white-grey dust in this capsule (right) is made of trillions of diamonds older than the solar system, the dust of ancient dying stars.

NATURAL HISTORY MUSEUM, MINERALOGY DEPARTMENT:
NHM 13989 (METEORITE)

101 Included diamond gemstone

A two-carat rectangular step-cut diamond with a large violet-red garnet inclusion visible in the table facet. This is an unusually attractive example of a diamond 'inclusion', a crystal, usually of another mineral, that became incorporated into the diamond as it grew. Such crystals can give valuable clues to the temperatures, pressures and rock types within which the diamond formed, and also help to date it. By examining inclusions, scientists learned that diamonds are far older than the kimberlite rock in which they are found at the surface.

NATURAL HISTORY MUSEUM, MINERALOGY DEPARTMENT:
NHM 1985, MI 36322

114 Surgical scalpel with blade of optical grade CVD material

Single CVD crystals of optical grade, grown and shaped for surgical blades. Diamond makes the ideal blade. It can be polished to the finest of edges, and will remain sharp far longer than steel. Its extreme optical transparency and tolerance of heat means that laser light can be directed through the crystal to cauterise as it cuts.

ELEMENT SIX LTD.

109, 115 Synthetic HPHT diamond grit samples and optical grade CVD diamond and applications

Scientists have been able to make diamond on an industrial scale since the 1950s by recreating the immense heat and high pressure found deep in the Earth. Later, they found an improved method, called Chemical Vapour Deposition (CVD), which involves heating carbon-rich gasses to very high temperatures in a near vacuum, building layers of micro-diamonds on a template surface, 'like frost growing on a window'. By controlling the mix, diamond films of complex 3D shapes, or single crystals, can be built to extremely tight specifications.

Synthetic diamond grit made by the high-pressure, high-temperature method (HPHT). The intense yellow colour is due to tiny traces of nitrogen, also responsible for yellow coloration in natural diamonds.

Optical grade CVD diamond 1/4 wafer – ultra-transparent when polished.

ELEMENT SIX LTD.

117 Diamond tweeter

Diamond, as well as being hard, is extremely stiff, and will transmit sound without distortion. This property has been put to use in developing the ultimate hi-fi tweeter (a small speaker designed to handle the highest frequencies). Its diamond diaphragm is grown on a precision-machined template, which is then removed, leaving the pure, perfectly formed diamond hemisphere.

B&W BOWERS AND WILKINS (TWEETER)
ELEMENT SIX LTD. (DIAPHRAGM)

122 World's smallest brilliant
0.0006 carats

This microscopically small diamond holds the world record for a complete, 58-faceted, brilliant-cut diamond. To cut it took remarkable skill.

MARJAN DIAMONDS, ANTWERP

123 The Excelsior I mounted in a sautoir
69.68 carats
South Africa
Sautoir jewel setting, Mouawad 2005

The second largest rough diamond ever discovered, at 995.2 carats, was found in a shovel load of gravel at the Jagersfontein Mine, South Africa, in 1893. The diamond was named the Excelsior and was cut into 21 gems, the largest being the Excelsior I. This magnificent pear-shaped stone with the characteristic blue-white colour of the finest stones from the mine is shown here mounted in a newly designed sautoir (a long necklace with pendant or tassel).

MOUAWAD, GENEVA (ON LOAN UNTIL 20 SEPT.)

124 The Black Orlov diamond pendant
67.5 carats
Setting and necklace white diamonds and platinum
Unknown origin, India?
Fred Nazz for Cartier, 1969

The origins of this black (actually gun-metal grey) diamond are mysterious. It is said to be named after the Russian princess Nadia Vyegin-Orlov, who owned it in the 18th century. Another story traces it to a 195-carat rough once set in a shrine in Pondicherry, India – its other name is The Eye of Brahma. Its confidently authenticated history begins only in the 1950s. In 1969, the Black Orlov was mounted in a brooch set with white diamonds, now suspended from a white diamond and platinum necklace. It has been exhibited widely, including at the American Museum of Natural History in Washington DC.

J. DENNIS PETIMEZAS, WATCHMAKERS DIAMONDS AND
JEWELRY, JOHNSTOWN, PENNSYLVANIA
(ON LOAN FROM 20 SEPT.)

135 Bracelet
Fancy and white diamonds, platinum
Moussaieff, 2005

A contemporary bracelet mounted in platinum, featuring an impressive collection of natural fancy-coloured, pear-shaped diamonds, hanging from a single row of three-carat brilliant-cut white diamonds. The largest pear is a 4.76 carat fancy grey-blue diamond, and the row contains intense pears of fancy pink, orangey yellows, intense and vivid yellows, fancy brownish pinks and so on, of graduated size down to 0.76 carats. Total diamond weight is 46.25 carats.

MOUSSAIEFF JEWELLERS

126 Neck collar
White gold, silver wire, diamonds
Christophe De Ranter, Antwerp, 1998

An extravagant collar inspired by the cartwheel collars of the Baroque period. Winner of the 1999 Antwerp Diamond High Council Competition *The Baroque and the Contemporary Diamond Jewel.*

DIAMOND MUSEUM, PROVINCE OF ANTWERP, INV. DMK. 01. 1

138 Heart-shaped evening purse
Gold, white, yellow and pink diamonds
Mouawad Legacy Collection

This diamond-encrusted purse was 'given' to actress Nicole Kidman by singer Robbie Williams in their video duet of a cover version of Frank and Nancy Sinatra hit *Somethin' Stupid*. She also wore an impressive Mouawad necklace, and the high value of these pieces meant security was very tight for the filming. The purse is part of the Mouawad Legacy Collection.

MOUAWAD, GENEVA

139 Portrait watch of R&B artist Usher
Diamonds, steel
Tiret, 2005

Usher's portrait is made up of natural fancy yellow diamonds, set on a background of white diamonds. Modelling the features required very careful selection of subtly varying shades of natural yellow diamonds. The total weight is 9.5 carats and there are 1106 stones including the bezel. The watch has two time zones, two dates, two chronographs and took more than seven months to make.

TIRET, NEW YORK (ON LOAN UNTIL 20 SEPT.)

128 Neckpiece
Platinum, diamonds
Total weight 68 carats
Dieter Huebner for Brinkhaus, 2000

This exuberant piece has exactly 2000 round brilliant-cut diamonds scattered on a graceful web of platinum wire. It represents both the majestic and the minute wonders of nature – the randomly placed stars of the Milky Way or dew drops glistening on a spider's web. Designed by Dieter Huebner of the Brinkhaus Jewellers Studio, it won a Diamonds-International Award in 2000.

BRINKHAUS JEWELS LTD.

142 Spiderman jewellery, and dress (replica)
Platinum, diamonds (in replica dress – crystal)
Scott Henshall, London, 2003
WebCut diamonds by Dali Diamonds, Antwerp

Seven 'spider' brooches were attached to the spectacular dress designed by Scott Henshall for the London première of the film *Spiderman II* on July 13, 2004. The dress had a 12-metre gold chain with 2400 diamonds, displayed as a 261-carat spider's web. A hand-covering ring like an enormous spider completed the set. All the major diamonds were WebCuts, a new cut created by Dali Diamonds. The spectacular right hand ring has 546 diamonds, with a central WebCut gem of 3.09 carats, and a total carat weight of 21.31 carats. The brooches range in size from 25 to 70 mm wide. The ensemble stole the show at the premiere party, where it was worn by Irish singer and actress Samantha Mumba.

JEWELS FROM DALI DIAMONDS, ANTWERP

144 Diamond thistle brooch
Gold, diamonds, L 120 mm
Paris, Octave Loeulliard for Frédéric Boucheron, 1880

A golden brooch in the shape of a realistic, inclining thistle leaf. Created for the great jewellery house, Boucheron, it was shown at the exhibition *Arts du Métal*, in 1880 in the Union des Arts Décoratifs in Paris. Boucheron said of Loeulliard, 'He is an exemplary worker. He is responsible for all my beautiful flowers in jewellery... he created my thistle, my masterwork'. This brooch is a clear exponent of the influence that nature studies and literature had on art and jewellery in the third quarter of the 19th century.

As thistles can grow in the harshest of environments, it became a symbol for long life and male vitality. It is also the emblem plant of Scotland, due to the legend that during an attack, a Viking chieftain stepped on a thistle and began to groan loudly, which awoke the Scots, allowing them to vanquish the enemy. In Christian faith, the thistle is a symbol for remorse and hope of redemption. In the 19th century, English peasant girls would ask the advice of a 'thistle oracle' if they could not decide between different suitors: a thistle shoot was placed under her pillow for every young man, and the one that began to root by morning was the winner.

FRED LEIGHTON RARE COLLECTIBLE JEWELS

154 Camellia brooch
Gold, silver, cloudy diamonds
Joel Arthur Rosenthal, 2005

A camellia brooch of cloudy diamonds, set in silver and gold. For 27 years, Joel Arthur Rosenthal has had a jewellery shop in Paris, and is often called 'the Fabergé of today'. This piece is typical of his masterful work.

JAR, PARIS

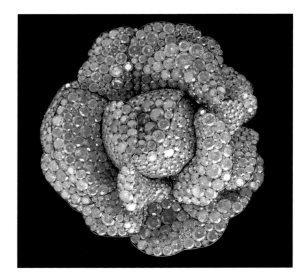

148 Panther demi-parure: bangle, brooch, pin
Platinum, diamonds, sapphires, emeralds, onyx,
Bangle 59 x 72 x 18 mm, brooch 54 x 27 mm, pin 96 x 30 mm
Cartier, Paris, 1957–58

The bangle consists of two jumping panthers, the clip brooch of a resting one, the jabot pin panther is sitting. They all have a body of *pavé*-set brilliants and cabochon sapphires, an onyx nose and emerald eyes. The bangle swivels to open. This eye-catching demi-parure belonged to Princess Sadruddin Aga Khan, a former fashion model (1930–65), who owned a substantial wardrobe of panther-skin clothing and jewellery, including another panther bracelet and ring. Cartier's panther is perhaps its most famous and instantly recognisable motif. It became popular in the 1940s under the direction of Jeanne Toussaint as a response to the drabness of the war years.

CARTIER COLLECTION

153 Skunk brooch
Stainless steel, black plastic, diamonds, rare earth magnet,
64 x 50 x 9 mm
Daniel Brush, 2005, signed

The white fur lines on the back and the tail of the skunk are suggested by a field of brilliants of very carefully selected sizes. This brooch is from the *La Ménagerie Magnétique* series, in which American artist, sculptor and jeweller Daniel Brush creates one-of-a-kind jewels inspired by America's 'hi-lo' culture and the fast-changing criteria of value and taste. They combine the beauty of nature with space-age materials and technology.

**DANIEL BRUSH,
NEW YORK**

145 Multi-coloured butterfly brooch
gold, fancy coloured diamonds, garnet
c. 1915?

An eight-carat yellow gold brooch mounted *en tremblant*, designed to create a sense of fluttering as it moves with the wearer. The brooch is set with an estimated 32 carats of old mine-cut diamonds of various colours, from pink to greens and yellows, browns and pale blue. The eyes are set with small demantoid garnets. The box has a fitted box with the name Collingwood on the inside. The indicated date is 1915.

MR V. JERLITSYN COLLECTION

List of loans

NB. Unless given otherwise all measurements are in mm.

1 The Steinmetz Pink
See p.22

2 The Heart of Eternity
See p.22

3 The Moussaieff Red
See p.23

4 The Ocean Dream
See p.23

5 The Orange Flame
See p.24

6 The Incomparable Diamond
See p.24

7 The 616
See p.25

8 The Allnatt
See p.25

9 The De Beers Millennium Star
See p.26

10 The Banjarmasin diamond
See p.27

11 Mogul-cut diamond
India
Single detached diamond showing old cut typical of Mogul style.
Fred Leighton Rare Collectible Jewels

12 Thumb ring
Almandine garnet, diamond, gold
Mogul, 17th century
Victoria and Albert Museum, inv. 02530(IS)

13 Belt buckle
Gold, enamel, diamonds
Rajasthan, India, 18th–19th century
Fashioned from highly refined gold in the *kundan* technique. Diamonds of various sizes are set into the outer surface. The reverse is decorated with enamel animal combats.
British Museum

14 'The Six Voyages of Jean-Baptiste Tavernier'
See p.27

15 The Shah Jahan diamond
See p.28

16 Portrait of Shah Jahan as a prince
See p.28

17 Turban ornament
Gold, enamel, emeralds, diamonds,
H 173, W 53
Probably second half of 17th century, India, probably Deccan (Hyderabad)
Turban ornament with enamels worked in *kundan* technique and set with emeralds and diamonds.
The al-Sabah Collection, Dar al-Althar al-Islamiyyah, Kuwait, LNS 1767 J

18 The Spanish Inquisition necklace
See p.29

19 Indian diamond and enamel necklace
See p.30

20 Elephant goad (*ankus*)
See p.30

21 Bracelet
Enamelled gold, diamonds
Dhaulpur, Rajasthan, c. 1850
Exhibited at the 1851 Great Exhibition as an example of 'modern' Indian work. Elaborate enamelling on reverse.
Victoria and Albert Museum, inv. 119–1852

22 Bazuband, an upper-arm bracelet
Platinum, diamonds, 143 x 130
Cartier, Paris, 1922
Could be worn as bracelet on upper arm or wrist, as pendant, brooch or corsage jewel.
Cartier Collection

23 Golconda diamond necklace
See p.30

24 Pendant with Jesus monogram
See p.31

25 Reliquary cross pendant
See p.31

26 Cross pendant
Gold and silver, diamonds, enamel,
37 x 27
The Netherlands, c. 1700
Cross of five full rose diamonds mounted in silver.
Victoria and Albert Museum, gift of Dame Joan Evans, inv. M. 74–1962

27 Pendant in the form of a lizard
See p.31

28 Peapod corsage brooch
See p.32

29 Corsage jewel
Gold, diamonds; engraved trailwork on back, W 170
Spain or Portugal, second half of 17th century
Wide, slightly banana-shaped jewel, probably for the bodice.
Diamond Museum, Province of Antwerp, inv. DMK 96/1

30 Girandole parure
See p.32

31 Bow stomacher
See p.33

32–34: Jewels belonging to the Brilliant Garnitur, one of several extravagant costume jewel sets of Augustus the Strong (1670–1733) and altered subsequently by his successors.
Staatliche Kunstsammlungen, Grünes Gewölbe, Dresden, Germany, inv. VIII 26, 21, 19 (on loan until 6 Dec.)

32 Aigrette or head jewel
Gold, silver, 359 diamonds in old brilliant cut, 148 x 94
Dresden, August Gotthelf, 1782–1807
Narrow fan-form aigrette with nine lines of diamonds, supported by a bow, in its middle a 7.05-carat brilliant. Possibly for a lady's head covering or a man's hunting hat.

33 Five vest buttons and five coat buttons
Silver, silver gilt, brilliants, diameter 19–20 and 24–25
Dresden, Ignaz Konrad Plödterl, 1827
Larger diamonds surrounded by smaller ones.

34 Two shoe buckles
See p.33

35 Golden Fleece Insignia
Gold, silver, opal cabochons, rose-cut diamonds, 141 x 68
Dresden, 1724
One of 11 Insignia of the Golden Fleece in the Green Vault. Opals were very rare and much-prized gemstones.
Staatliche Kunstsammlungen, Grünes Gewölbe, Dresden, Germany, inv. VIII 2 (on loan until 6 Dec.)

36 Three separated diamonds from a Golden Fleece Insignia
Old-cut yellow brilliants: pendeloque 13.30 carats, square 23.30 carats, round 13.85 carats
From a Golden Fleece Insignia made in 1731 and disassembled in 1806.
Staatliche Kunstsammlungen, Grünes Gewölbe, Dresden, Germany, inv. VIII 27.d,b,c (on loan until 6 Dec.)

37–39: Rings almost certainly belonging to the case of 25 precious rings, which always accompanied Augustus the Strong (1670–1733) on his travels.
Staatliche Kunstsammlungen, Grünes Gewölbe, Dresden, Germany, inv. VIII 45, 46, 50 (on loan until 6 Dec.)

37 Ring with a pink old brilliant
Gold, silver, diamonds, H 26
Before 1733
Pink pear-shaped old-cut brilliant surrounded by eleven old-cut brilliants added in 1763.

38 Ring with a light-green old brilliant
Gold, silver, diamonds, H 26
Large light-green diamond surrounded by 22 smaller white brilliants.

39 Ring with light-blue old brilliant
Gold, silver, diamonds, H 25
Early 18th century
Large, light blue old-cut brilliant surrounded by 15 smaller white brilliants.

40 Aigrette
See p.34

41 Necklace of rosettes and small sprays
See p.34

42 Flower branch hairpin or brooch
Gold, silver, diamonds, 150 x 30
England, late 18th–early 19th century
Hair jewel or brooch, can also be dismantled into three parts.
Diamond Museum, Province of Antwerp, inv. DMK 98/6

43 Queen Consort Henrietta Maria's ring
Gold, diamond, enamel, diameter 26
England, 1628–29?
Ring with lozenge table diamond engraved with arms of Henrietta Maria, Queen Consort of Charles I.
Lent by Her Majesty The Queen

44 Garter Star
See p.35

45 Ring with miniature portrait of King George III
Gold, diamonds, miniature on ivory, 18 x 22 x 22
England, miniature by Jeremiah Meyer, 1761
Rounded square miniature showing the King in profile, surrounded by old-cut brilliants. Presented to Queen Charlotte by King George III.
Lent by Her Majesty The Queen, inv. RCIN 62211

46 Order of the Garter Badge (Great George)
See p.35

47 Queen Victoria's Order of the Garter Sash Badge (Lesser George)
Gold, diamonds, brown-on-grey cameo, 130 x 68
England, c. 1790–1810 (Marchant?)
Framed cameo, with diamond buckle and bow.
Lent by Her Majesty The Queen, inv. RCIN 441152

48 The Murchison snuff box
See p.36

49 Original plaster cast of the Koh-i-Noor before recutting and two additional casts of pendant diamonds
See p.36

50 Lead moulds and glass model of the Pitt or Regent diamond
London, 1760?
Lead moulds made at stages during the cutting of the Pitt diamond, later sold to the Regent of France, as figured in *The General Contents of the British Museum*, 1762, p97.
Natural History Museum, Mineralogy Department: Lead moulds – inv. NHM 85433-5; Glass model – inv. NHM 85432

51 The Thurn und Taxis four rivières necklace
See p.37

52 Wreath tiara or necklace
See p.37

53 Golden spray brooch with a larger and a smaller flower
See p.38

54 Branch brooch with an eglantine en tremblant
See p.38

55 Spray brooch with a flower
See p.38

56 Parure with a stomacher in three parts
Gold, silver, diamonds; corsage in three parts: 240 x 102, bracelet; tiara 240 x 60; earrings 5
France? Mid 19th century
With *en tremblant* elements. The corsage could be split to wear as three separate brooches, the bracelet was worn also as a diadem.
Antwerp, private collection

57 Devant de corsage or bodice ornament of two lily sprays
See p.39

58 The Eureka
See p.40

59 The Star of South Africa
See p.40

60 Fabergé tiara
See p.41

61 Tiara with interlacing sprays
Platinum, diamonds.
France? c. 1910
Tiara in the garland style, with old mine-cut and rose-cut diamonds. Worn by Catherine Zeta-Jones at her wedding to Michael Douglas in November 2000.
Fred Leighton Rare Collectible Jewels

62 Diamond corsage ornament
See p.42

63 Hexagonal pendant/brooch
See p.42

64 Sunburst tiara
See p.41

65 Art deco strap bracelet
Platinum, diamonds, L 187
Paris, made by Sauvan for Cartier, 1923
Flexible bracelet composed of a graduated row of box-set cushion-shaped diamonds alternating with old-European-cut diamonds, the centre and clasp having a circular motif set with rose- and old-cut diamonds.
Cartier Collection

66 Art deco bracelet-watch with concealed dial
Platinum, diamonds, L 180
Paris, Jaeger and Lavabre for Cartier, 1929
Articulated bracelet of geometrical stepped motifs alternating with open square links, the dial concealed by a hinged cover set with square diamonds and a larger elongated step-cut diamond at the centre.
Cartier Collection

67 Diamond earrings
Platinum, diamond
c. 1940–50
Each set with very large, pear-shape brilliant-cut diamond and smaller baguette-cut diamonds. The large diamonds cut probably in the 1920s or 1930s, the setting later and unmarked.
British Museum, inv. 2001, 5-5, 8

68 Seven jewels to illustrate the evolution of diamond cuts
See p.43

69 'Power of Love' ring collection
See p.44

70 Ring with lily motif
Gold, diamonds, enamel;
bezel 17 x 14, ring diameter 22
Possibly French, 17th century
Five fancy table-cut diamonds forming the fleur-de-lys of the French Royal Court. Held in bezel between two buttons decorated with (presumably) a simple coat of arms: an azure field with a vertical bar of silver.
Private collection, Belgium

71 Ring with 15 table diamonds
Gold, diamonds, enamel, 24 x 20, case 19 x 12
France? second half of the 17th century
Fifteen table diamonds arranged in a lozenge on top; sides and underside ornamented with flower motif in black and white enamel.
Private collection, Belgium

72 Blue diamond solitaire
See p.44

73 Cartier ring
Gold, platinum, diamonds, onyx, 33 x 20 x 26
Cartier, Paris, 1949
Shank carved in black onyx around gold central band. Shoulders and top pavé-set with brilliants and baguettes. Centre has larger oval brilliant between two halfmoon-shaped diamonds.
Cartier Collection

74 Solitaire ring
Platinum, diamond, c. 1954
Cartier, London
Platinum solitaire ring with rectangular-cut corner trap-cut diamond, flanked on each side by one small baguette-cut diamond.
British Museum, inv. 2001, 5-5, 9

75 Ring
Bakelite, diamonds, H 38
Daniel Brush, 1986
Domed bakelite ring set with marquise- and pear-cut, fancy coloured diamonds, and inlaid with steel balls.
Collection of Janet Zapata

76 Diamond cube ring
Diamond, black acrylic and platinum
Manfred Seitner, Austria, 1990
Cube set in unpolished black acrylic and platinum set with 42 square-cut diamonds weighing 10.95 carats.
Winner, Diamonds-International Awards, 1990.
The Diamond Trading Company

77 Ring for the little finger
Yellow gold, platinum, iron, ebony, sunflower-cut diamond, H 46
Antwerp, Georges Cuyvers, 1993
Specially designed to keep the fancy-cut diamond upright when worn.
Diamond Museum, Province of Antwerp, inv. DMK 94.1

78 Portrait diamond ring
See p.44

79 The Tearcatcher ring
White gold, 2 carats brilliant-cut diamonds
London, Shaun Leane and Sam Taylor Wood, 2003
The tear-shaped scoop in the ring can be used for catching tears, which can be kept in the small corked vials in a leather box, as a memory of an emotional event.
Shaune Leane in collaboration with Sam Taylor-Wood for the Louisa Guinness Gallery

80 Gold 'Funnel' ring
Diamond, gold
Joel Arthur Rosenthal, 2005
A gold 'funnel' ring set with a cushion-shaped diamond.
JAR, Paris

81 Aurora Collection and Aurora Additions
See p.45

82 Historic diamond prospecting samples
Sands and gravels, indicator minerals, peridotite, concentrates, kimberlites
From the Natural History Museum's Mineralogy Collections, collected by geologists in southern Africa in the late 19th and early 20th century.
Natural History Museum, Mineralogy Department

83 Brazilian diamond crystals
Diamond in gold; diamond in ferruginous conglomerate
Brazil, acquired 1833 and 1877
Rare early Brazilian samples: small octahedral crystal in native gold, and small crystal in conglomerate of quartz, chert and other minerals.
Natural History Museum, Mineralogy Department: NHM 57182, NHM 51170

84 Diamond in 'yellow ground'
See p.46

85 Diamonds in conglomerate
Alexander Bay, Namaqualand, Northern Cape, South Africa
Two small crystals enclosed in conglomerate from marine terraces (presented to NHM 1937).
Natural History Museum, Mineralogy Department: NHM 1985, MI26784

86 Octahedron in matrix
Approximately 40 carats, South Africa
Large diamond crystal as found in kimberlite matrix.
De Beers Consolidated Mines

87 The Aber diamond
See p.46

88 Canadian rough diamonds
200 carats
Diavik, Northern Territories, Canada
Selection of rough crystals to show quality of Canadian finds.
Aber Diamond Corporation

89 'Run-of-mine'
See p.47

90 Diamond crystal forms
A variety of natural forms, from balls and cubes to stars, crosses, and irregular masses.
The Diamond Trading Company

91 Flattened crystal
19.9 carats, South Africa
An unusual elongated and flattened octahedral crystal, found at Kimberley, South Africa.
Natural History Museum, Mineralogy Department: NHM 1923, 3

92 Coloured diamonds
A variety of coloured diamond roughs from greens, pinks and blues to yellows and browns.
The Diamond Trading Company

93 Coloured diamonds
A variety of diamond crystals of different colours, many 'fancy' intense colours.
Natural History Museum, Mineralogy Department

94 Bracelet
Unpolished platinum, gold and copper, diamonds (total weight 4.31 carats)
Norbert Muerrle, 1984
Bracelet interspersed with copper and gold flecks, brilliant-cut, baguettes, triangles, lozenge, square- and princess-cut diamonds, of white and natural colours. Winner, Diamonds-International Awards, 1984. Sponsored by Niessing, Vreden.
The Diamond Trading Company

95 Kimberlite series
Yellow ground (upper levels); blue ground (677 m and 1073 m deep)
Series of three rock samples illustrating change in kimberlite at different depths in a pipe.
Natural History Museum, Mineralogy Department: NHM 1985, MI 8651; NHM 1910, 552(10); NHM 1929, 1653

96 Diamond sources
Kimberlite, lamproite, sand and gravel deposits
Collection of secondary (gravels and sands) and primary (kimberlite and lamproite) deposit samples representing some key sources of diamond across the world.
Natural History Museum, Mineralogy Department

97 Cañon Diablo meteorite
Coconino Co., Northern Arizona
Meteorite fragment, contains microscopic diamonds formed on impact.
Natural History Museum, Mineralogy Department: NHM 67592, acquired 1891

98–99 Cold Bokkeveld meteorite and diamond dust extracted from meteorite
See p.48

100 Imilac meteorite, polished slice
Atacama Desert, Chile
Stony-iron meteorite composed of material similar to that of the primeval Earth. Large lime-green olivine crystals embedded in a nickel-iron matrix.
Natural History Museum, Mineralogy Department: NHM 53322

101 Included diamond gemstone
See p.48

102 Heavily included modified crystal
Colourless, modified 'spinel-twinned' crystal, with mass of inclusions and flaws.
Natural History Museum, Mineralogy Department: NHM 25030 (Part of the H.P. Hope Collection, purchased from Mr Tennant, 1849)

103 Octahedral crystal with 'carbon spot'
Very faint blue, clear octahedral diamond crystal with central 'carbon spot' inclusion.
Natural History Museum, Mineralogy Department: NHM 25057 (Part of the H.P. Hope Collection, purchased from Mr Tennant, 1849)

104 Included diamond gemstone
Old-cut brilliant of a pale yellow colour showing several dark 'carbon spot' inclusions.
Natural History Museum, Mineralogy Department: NHM 1988, 90

105 Synthetic and natural diamond of industrial grade
40,000 carats of synthetics. Today, natural diamond accounts for only 1% of the global market in industrial diamonds.
Element Six Ltd.

106 Chemical Vapour Deposition (CVD) diamond, growth series
Silicon disc, disc with deposit of diamond, diamond wafers
In the CVD process, diamond is deposited onto silicon templates, and the resulting wafer of diamond then removed.
Diamond Electronics Group, University College London

107 CVD nanodiamond wafer
Nanodiamonds a thousand times smaller than those in a polycrystalline CVD wafer, grown at lower temperatures, so that a far smoother surface is created.
Diamond Electronics Group, University College London

108 The Hannay diamonds
Nine crystals, *c.* 1880 (no. of crystals is in a reliable bk. TBC)
Historically important microscopic shards of diamond, thought for years to be the first synthetic diamonds made. Finally confirmed as natural diamond in 1962.
Natural History Museum, Mineralogy Department: NHM 87756

109 Synthetic HPHT diamond grit samples
Variety of grits grown to very tight specifications for different industrial applications.
See p.49
Element Six Ltd.

110 Polycrystalline diamond (PCD) samples and tools
PCD discs and cut segments.
PCD-tipped twist drill.
PCD router for woodworking.

111 Grinding and drilling tools using industrial diamond
Multipoint wheel dresser.
Surface set drill bit.
Element Six Ltd.

112 Mechanical grade CVD diamond wafer
Element Six Ltd.

113 Monocrystal diamond tool
For machining contact lenses.

114 Fine cutting tools
Surgical scalpel with blade of optical grade CVD material (See p.49)
Surgical blades - five single crystal and five cut from CVD wafer.
Ultramicrotome cradles set with diamond blades.
Element Six Ltd.

115 Optical grade CVD diamond and applications
Grade used as 'windows' for high-powered lasers and in infra-red devices that monitor composition of aggressive materials such as molten plastics.
Optical grade CVD diamond, one quarter wafer
See p.49
Two infrared windows.
Diamond slice, window for CO_2 laser.
Element Six Ltd.

116 Thermal and electronic applications for CVD diamond
Ten heat spreaders – diamond dissipates heat rapidly in electronics
Three etalons – vital wave-locking filters for the internet
Element Six Ltd.
CVD diamond transistor, biosensor, UV detector – new applications
Diamond Electronics Group, University College London

117 Diamond tweeter
See p.49

118 Diamond cutting tools
Suite of tools traditionally used for cutting diamonds. Similar tools are still in use today.
Diamond Museum, Province of Antwerp, Belgium

119 Rough and cut diamonds
Comparative series illustrating the link between natural crystal shape and the shape of a gemstone cut from it.
The Diamond Trading Company

120 Cutting series: rough macle to diamond Buddha
Buddha diamond Cut Co. (Antwerp), A. Haberkorn & Sons (Antwerp), J. Kleinhaus & Sons (New York), Precious Stones Co. (Benjamin Zucker, New York)

121 Cutting series: rough macle to final trilliant
A. Haberkorn & Sons (Antwerp), J. Kleinhaus & Sons (New York), Precious Stones Co. (Benjamin Zucker, New York)

122 World's smallest brilliant
See p.50

123 The Excelsior I mounted in a sautoir
See p.50

124 The Black Orlov diamond pendant
See p.51

125 'Mijn getemde Koning' (my domesticated king) necklace
Yellow gold, rubber, diamonds (102 brilliants, total weight 1.08 carats)
diameter 110
Georges Cuyvers, Antwerp, 1995
Sets the notion of daily bread (a 'king' in Belgian is a flat, round loaf of bread) against the choice of costly materials, gold and diamond.
Diamond Museum, Province of Antwerp, inv. DMK 99.10

126 Neck collar
See p.52

127 'Dances of Water' necklace
White gold, diamonds (total weight 48.88 carats)
Jiang Bao Luo, 2004, China
Inspired by the movement of light over water. Diamonds: Nature's Miracle Collection. Sponsored by The Old Temple Gold Co. Ltd.
The Diamond Trading Company
(on loan from 6 Dec.)

128 Neckpiece
See p.53

129 'The Countess'
Diamonds, gold, L 310

Michelle Ong for Carnet
Necklace of fancy brown rose-cut diamonds, mounted in 18-carat gold.
Carnet

130 Earrings
Gold, platinum, diamonds (total weight 12.8 carats)
Yoko Yoshida, Japan, 1986
Asymmetric torpedo shapes, in 18-carat yellow gold and in platinum, set with 12 and 23 brilliants. Sponsored by Tasaki Shinju Co. Ltd. Diamonds-International Awards 1986.
The Diamond Trading Company

131 'Eiffel Tower'
platinum, diamond, L 125, W 45
Michelle Ong for Carnet, 2002
368 white rose-cut diamonds with a total weight of 18.99 carats mounted in platinum.
Carnet

132 Brooch
White gold, fire-rose-cut diamond, L 90
Lucie Bausart, 1996
Winner of the Antwerp Diamond High Council Competition, 1996, using a diamond cut in a new design.
Diamond Museum, Province of Antwerp, inv. DMK 99.11

133 'Nebula' brooch
Diamond, black and pink gold
Chiara Colombani, Italy, 2004
Created using 180 carats of diamonds, black and pink gold, with a magnetic clasp and Leo-cut diamonds. Designed to be worn with an alpaca cloak by Lanificio Colombo. Diamonds: Nature's Miracle Collection. Diamonds by Schachter & Namdar.
The Diamond Trading Company

134 'Ode to the Tango' wrist or ankle bracelet
Silver plate, metallic fabric and cord, 30 0.25-carat marquise cut diamonds
Frans Switsers, 2001
Inspired by the folded gauze of the bandonion, a small accordion used in tango orchestras. Winner of the Antwerp Diamond High Council Competition 'Memories'.

Diamond Museum, Province of Antwerp, on loan from the HRD

135 Bracelet
See p.51

137 'Diamond dip'
Diamond, platinum, L 180, W 90
Michelle Ong for Carnet, 2002
Platinum bracelet inlaid with 1098 white rose-cut diamonds weighing 60.35 carats.
Carnet

138 Heart-shaped evening purse
See p.52

139 Portrait watch of R&B artist Usher
See p.52

140 Invisible-set diamond pen
Gold, diamonds (total weight 71.6 carats)
Siegelson & Spectra Gems Ltd., 1999
Entire pen 'invisible set' with princess-cut diamonds, accented at ends with two octagonal-cut diamonds, mounted in 18-carat gold.
Private collection

141 Pair of diamond 'black lace' cuff bracelets
Silver, platinum, white gold, 3184 diamonds (total weight 44.29 carats)
L 101.6
Designed by Michelle Ong for Carnet, 2000
Simulated *peau de soie* bands embellished with collet-set diamonds, offset by scroll and bracket diamond line borders and openwork ruffle of diamond foliates.
Private collection

142 Spiderman jewellery and dress (replica)
See p.53

143 Snake jewel, necklace or bracelet
Gold, diamonds, rubies, enamel, L 467, head 50 x 24
France? *c.* 1860
Golden-bodied snake with head inlaid with 18 old-cut brilliants, two rose-cut diamonds for the eyes and

little rubies on the tongue.
Diamond Museum, Province of Antwerp, inv. DMK 99/4

144 Diamond thistle brooch
See p.54

145 Multi-coloured butterfly brooch
See p.55

146 Dragonfly brooch
Gold, diamonds, ruby, emeralds
Early 20th century
Diamond-set body accentuated with rows of small emeralds.
Mr V Jerlitsyn Collection

147 Flower clip brooch
White gold, platinum, diamonds, L 125
Paris, Cartier, 1950s
The flexible stem carries a daisy-like flower, fully covered with old- and single-cut brilliants.
Cartier Collection

148 Panther demi-parure: bangle, brooch, pin
See p.55

149 'The Snake' necklace
White gold, yellow gold, platinum, diamonds (total weight 178.21 carats), emeralds, enamel, L 570
Paris, Cartier, 1968
Technically virtuoso piece designed for Mexican actress and diva Maria Felix (1914–2002): on the movable body and head, 2473 baguette diamonds; the head also has large brilliants. The eyes are emeralds, the underside is composed of green, black and red enamelled layers.
Cartier Collection

150 Brooch with trumpet flowers
Gold, diamonds
Etsuko Sonobe, 1982
18-carat yellow gold with three pear-shaped diamonds weighing 1 carat, and 57 brilliant-cut diamonds weighing 6.8 carats, delicately set in the form of diamond flowers.
Diamonds-International Awards, 1982.
The Diamond Trading Company

151–154 Jewels from La Ménagerie // Magnétique series

151 Panther on 'branch' brooch
Stainless steel, black plastic, yellow-brown, black and white diamonds, rare earth magnet, 50 x 75 x 9
Daniel Brush, New York, 2004, signed

152 Poodle brooch
Stainless steel, beige plastic, yellow-brown diamonds, rare earth magnet, 70 x 50 x 9
Daniel Brush, New York, 2004, signed

153 Skunk brooch
See p.55

154 Camellia brooch
See p.54

155 Dragonfly brooch
Silver, gold, diamond
Joel Arthur Rosenthal, 2005
Dragonfly brooch in silver and gold, set with two large Golconda diamonds and smaller diamonds.
JAR, Paris

156 Graphite and diamond necklace
Coal, diamond, platinum
Cornelia Rating, 2000
Platinum and coal necklace set with 1528 black and white diamonds weighing 71.8 carats. Diamonds-International Awards, 2000.
Sponsors: Hahn Söhne and H. Gilroy & Söhne.
See p.19
Cornelia Rating

157 Copy of the original Koh-i-Noor
Cubic zirconia
Based on extensive study of the 1851 model.
John Nels Hatleberg

Further reading

An Illustrated Dictionary of Jewelry, Harold Newman.
Thames & Hudson, London, 2000, 2003. ISBN 0 500 27452 5.

Diamants: Au Cœur de la Terre, au Cœur des Étoiles, au Cœur du Pouvoir, Hubert Bari & Violaine Sautter (eds). Adam Biro, Paris, 2001. ISBN 2 87660 301 2. English edition, Vilo International, Paris, 2001. ISBN: 2 84576 032 9.

Diamonds, Eric Bruton. N A G Press, London, 1981, 1987, 1993. ISBN: 0 801 96789 9.

Diamond: The History of a Cold-Blooded Love Affair, Matthew Hart. HarperCollins Publishers, 2003. ISBN: 1 84115 280 3.

Dictionnaire International du Bijou, Marguerite de Cerval (ed). Regard, Paris, 1998. ISBN 2 903370 98 2.

Jewellery in Britain, 1066 – 1837: A Documentary, Social, Literary and Artistic Survey, Diana Scarisbrick. Michael Russell Publishing, Norwich, 1994. ISBN 0 85955 190 3.

Jewellery: The International Era 1789–1910, Shirley Bury. 2 vols. Antique Collector's Club, Woodbridge, 1997, 2002. ISBN 1 85149 104 X.

Jewelry: From Antiquity to the Present, Claire Phillips. Thames & Hudson, London, 1996. ISBN 0 500 20287 7.

Living Diamonds. Fauna and Flora in Diamond Jewellery, Jan Walgrave. Exhibition catalogue. HRD, Antwerp, 2002.

Precious Gems: Jewellery from Eight Centuries. Exhibition catalogue. National Museum, Stockholm, 2000.

Rings: Symbols of Wealth, Power and Affection, Diana Scarisbrick. Thames & Hudson, London, 1993. ISBN 0 500 01563 5.

The Diamond Makers, Robert M. Hazen. Cambridge University Press, 1999. ISBN: 0 521 65474 2.

The Nature of Diamonds, George E. Harlow (ed). Cambridge University Press, 1997. ISBN: 0 521 62935 7.

The Splendour of Diamond: 400 Years of Diamond Jewellery in Europe, Jan Walgrave. Exhibition catalogue. APT International, Tokyo, 2003. ISBN 4 901357 39 3.

Tiaras: A History of Splendour, Geoffrey C. Munn. The Antique Collector's Club, Woodbridge, 2001. ISBN 1 85177 359 2.

Picture credits

©Aurora Gems/Photo Robert Weldon: cat no.81 (emerald-cut); ©B&W Bowers & Wilkins: cat no.117; ©British Museum: cat no.72; ©Bruce M. White: cat no.15; ©C. Creutz: cat no.59; Chris Alderman ©Diamond Trading Company Ltd.: p.19, cat no.69; ©Chuck Mamula Photography: cat no.124; ©Cool Diamonds.com: cat no.23; ©Cora Diamond Corporation: cat no.4; ©De Beers: cat no.7, 58; ©De Beers LV Ltd.: cat no.9; ©Diamond Trading Company Ltd.: cat no.89; Harlow, *The Nature of Diamonds*, 1998 ©CUP: p.9; ©Herzog Anton Ulrich Museum: p.14; ©Jacques Sonck, PMF, Antwerp: cat no.25, 27, 30; ©Johan Carlens/Diamond Museum: cat no.40; ©Joris Certiaens & Kurt De Wit/Diamond Museum: cat no.126; ©Moussaieff Jewellers Ltd.: cat no.3, 135; ©National Museum of Natural History, Smithsonian Institution: cat no.18; Photo Nick Welsh, Cartier Collection ©Cartier: cat no.57, 63, 148; ©Paul Louis, Brussels: cat no.41, 53, 54, 55; ©Reserved: cat no.10, 62, 78, 122, 128, 142, 154; ©Robert Weldon: cat no.5; The Royal Collection ©2005 Her Majesty Queen Elizabeth II: cat no.44, 46; Courtesy of Sotheby's: cat no.51; ©Staatliche Kunstsammlungen Dresden: cat no.31, 34; ©The Steinmetz Diamond Group: p.7, cat no.1, 2; From *Tiaras: Past and Present*, Geoffrey Munn: cat no.60, 64; ©Tiret New York: cat no.139; ©V&A Images/Victoria and Albert Museum: cat no.16, 20, 24, 28, 52. **All other images ©2005 Natural History Museum, London.**

First published by the Natural History Museum, Cromwell Road, London SW7 5BD
© Natural History Museum, London, 2005

ISBN 0 565 09201 4

A catalogue record for this book is available from the British Library.

Designed by Mercer Design
Cover designed by the Design Studio, Natural History Museum
Reproduction and printing by Witherbys, UK

Front cover image: The De Beers Millennium Star (see p.26)